Office of the Deputy Prime Minister
Creating sustainable communities

Mental Health and Social Exclusion

Social Exclusion Unit Report

Social Exclusion Unit

June 2004

Office of the Deputy Prime Minister, London

The Office of the Deputy Prime Minister
Eland House
Bressenden Place
London SW1E 5DU
Telephone 020 7944 4400
Web site www.odpm.gov.uk
www.socialexclusionunit.gov.uk

Further copies of this publication are available from:
ODPM Publications
PO Box 236
Wetherby LS23 7NB
Tel: 0870 1226 236
Fax: 0870 1226 237
Textphone: 0870 1207 405
Email: odpm@twoten.press.net
Online: www.publications.odpm.gov.uk

ISBN: 1851127178

Printed in Great Britain on material containing 75% post-consumer waste and 25% ECF pulp

June 2004

Product code: 04 SEU 02280

CONTENTS

Prime Minister's Foreword

Millions of people suffer from mental health conditions some time in their lives. For a minority, these can be severe or long-lasting. Even now, with welcome new attitudes in society, those suffering mental distress still find themselves excluded from many aspects of life the rest of us take for granted – from jobs, family support, proper health care and community life.

This exclusion has a huge impact on the individuals concerned and on our wider society. It frequently leads to a downward spiral of unemployment, poverty, family breakdown and deteriorating health. The costs to individuals, their families and the country are huge, not just now but also in the future. Disadvantage, too, often passes from one generation to the next.

Nowhere is this more likely than in our most deprived neighbourhoods where mental health conditions are more common and their potential impact greatest. There are also particular barriers and problems faced by those from ethnic minorities.

None of this is something any Government committed to building a fairer and more inclusive society can ignore. We have already put in place far-reaching measures to improve NHS mental health services, strengthened civil rights and increased support to help people back into work. Community initiatives, often led by an expert and innovative voluntary sector, have been encouraged. But we need to do more if we are to ensure all can share in our rising prosperity and increasing opportunity.

That is why the Government asked the Social Exclusion Unit to examine how we could better attack the cycle of deprivation linked to mental health. The comprehensive programme outlined in this report sets out how we can improve health and well being, boost employment and training, increase support to families and prevent the isolation of those with mental health conditions. It will also ensure greater help is given in finding permanent homes – vital for the recovery and successful integration of those with mental health conditions.

The report calls on all Government departments and agencies to work together more effectively than in the past. We must rise to the task. But it also requires determined action to end the stigma of mental health – a challenge not just for Government but for all of us.

Tony Blair

Tony Blair

Summary

> *"For some of us, an episode of mental distress will disrupt our lives so that we are pushed out of the society in which we were fully participating. For others, the early onset of distress will mean social exclusion throughout our adult lives, with no prospect of training for a job or hope of a future in meaningful employment. Loneliness and loss of self-worth lead us to believe we are useless, and so we live with this sense of hopelessness, or far too often choose to end our lives. Repeatedly when we become ill we lose our homes, we lose our jobs and we lose our sense of identity. Not only do we cost the government money directly in health, housing and welfare payments, we lose the ability to contribute our skills and economically through taxes.*
>
> *"So we are perceived as a social burden. We lose sight of our potential, and when we try to move on, discrimination and stigma prevent us getting jobs that use our skills and experience and push us out of housing and education. The jobs we do get are poorly paid, and don't utilise our skills and experience. And there are practical considerations – we stand to lose our financial security, whether state benefits or private insurance, when we attempt to rebuild our lives. We also stand to lose the health and social services that we find helpful, so that at the time when we most need support, our coping mechanisms are undermined. Moving back into society becomes a risky business."*

The problem

1. Adults with mental health problems are one of the most excluded groups in society. Although many want to work, fewer than a quarter actually do – the lowest employment rate for any of the main groups of disabled people.[1] Too often people do not have other activities to fill their days and spend their time alone.

2. Mental health problems are estimated to cost the country over £77 billion a year through the costs of care, economic losses and premature death.[2] Early intervention to keep people in work and maintain social contacts can significantly reduce these costs. Once a person has reached crisis point, it is much more difficult and costly to restore their employment and social status.

3. Social isolation is an important risk factor for deteriorating mental health and suicide. Two-thirds of men under the age of 35 with mental health problems who die by suicide are unemployed.[3]

4. Severe mental health problems, such as schizophrenia, are relatively rare affecting around one in 200 adults each year,[4] although they can also have a wider impact on the lives of friends and family.

5. Depression, anxiety and phobias can affect up to one in six of the population at any one time,[5] with the highest rates in deprived neighbourhoods.[6] GPs spend a third of their time on mental health issues.[7] Prescription costs for anti-depressant drugs have risen significantly in recent years,[8] and there are significant variations in access to talking therapies.

6. Over 900,000 adults in England claim sickness and disability benefits for mental health conditions, with particularly high claimant rates in the North.[9] This group is now larger than the total number of unemployed people claiming Jobseekers' Allowance in England.[10] Individual Placement and Support programmes in the US have achieved employment rates of over 50 per cent among people with severe mental health problems,[11] but these have not been widely implemented in this country.

7. Mental health problems can have a particularly strong impact on families – both financially and emotionally. Carers themselves are twice as likely to have mental health problems if they provide substantial care.[12] An estimated 6,000 to 17,000 children and young people care for an adult with mental health problems.[13]

8. Creating sustainable, inclusive communities is about everyone having a stake. Being in work and having social contacts is strongly associated with improved health and well-being. People with mental health problems have much to offer. If they are able to fulfil their potential, the impact of mental health problems on individuals, their families and society can be significantly reduced.

The causes

9. The Social Exclusion Unit has identified five main reasons why mental health problems too often lead to and reinforce social exclusion:

- **Stigma and discrimination** against people with mental health problems is pervasive throughout society. Despite a number of campaigns, there has been no significant change in attitudes.[14] Fewer than four in ten employers say they would recruit someone with a mental health problem.[15] Many people fear disclosing their condition, even to family and friends.

- Professionals across sectors too often have **low expectations** of what people with mental health problems can achieve. There is limited recognition in the NHS that returning to work and overcoming social isolation is associated with better health outcomes. Employment is not seen as a key objective for people with mental health problems by many health and social care professionals.

- There is a **lack of clear responsibility** for promoting vocational and social outcomes for adults with mental health problems. Services do not always work effectively together to meet individual needs and maximise the impact of available resources.

- People can **lack ongoing support to enable them to work**. £140 million a year is invested by health and social care in vocational and day services for people with mental health problems.[16] But not all of these promote social inclusion as effectively as they could, and links with Jobcentre Plus can be weak. People on benefits often do not believe they will end up financially better off if they try to move into work. Many people lose jobs that they might have kept had they received better support.

- People face **barriers to engaging in the community**. They can struggle to access the basic services they need, in particular decent housing and transport. Education, arts, sports and leisure providers often are not aware how their services could benefit people with mental health problems and how they could make their services more accessible for this group. Many people do not want to participate in activities alone, but feel there is no one they can ask to go with them. People can also face exclusion by law from some community roles such as jury service.

10. Some groups face particular barriers to getting their mental health and social needs addressed:

- **ethnic minorities** may feel alienated from mainstream (predominantly white) mental health services, and so tend to present late to mental health services. They have often had contact with the criminal justice system, are more likely to disagree with their diagnosis, and can encounter discrimination on grounds of both health status and ethnicity in seeking work;

- **young men** with mental health problems are at high risk of dropping out of education or work, of becoming involved with crime, and they are a particularly high risk group for suicide;

- **parents** with mental health problems – particularly lone parents – have very low employment rates,[17] may not receive sufficient family support and their children may develop emotional problems;[18] and

- **adults with complex needs**, such as substance misuse or homelessness in addition to their mental health problems, often struggle to get their needs met by statutory services.[19]

Progress so far

11. There are already a number of important measures in place that contribute to tackling social exclusion among adults with mental health problems, in particular:

- the *Pathways to Work* pilots are providing a radical new approach to supporting incapacity benefit claimants back into work;

- the *National Service Framework for Mental Health* is driving a major programme of reform of mental health services. Implementation is supported by the National Institute for Mental Health in England, whose work recognises the importance of promoting social inclusion; and

- the *Disability Discrimination Act 1995* which outlaws discrimination against disabled people.

12. There are a number of places across the country where innovative work, often led by the voluntary and community sector, is making a significant impact on health outcomes and employment rates. Some areas, such as South West London and St George's Mental Health Trust, have implemented Individual Placement and Support programmes based on the US model with encouraging results. Successful local projects are characterised by close partnership working between agencies, a clear focus on the aspirations of the individual and strong local leadership.

13. People who are at increased risk of social exclusion are among those most likely to have mental health problems. At national level, some of the most important drivers of social exclusion are being tackled, reducing the overall number of people at risk. There have been important successes in tackling the causes and effects of social exclusion and in preventing further increases in inequality, as set out in the Social Exclusion Unit's emerging findings paper, *Tackling Social Exclusion: Taking stock and looking to the future.*[20] The Strategy Unit is currently undertaking a project with the aim of improving the life chances of disabled people.

- Employment has increased by more than **1.9 million** in the last seven years, with unemployment now at 4.7 per cent, compared to 9.1 per cent ten years ago.[21] The forthcoming Social Exclusion Unit report on *Jobs and Enterprise in Deprived Areas* will set out evidence on the local areas still suffering from very high levels of worklessness, and what more government plans to do about them.

- The number of children living in relative low income households has fallen by 500,000 since 1997.[22] The government is also strengthening services for children where mental health problems often emerge, through *Every Child Matters*[23] and increasing investment in Child and Adolescent Mental Health Services.

- There has been a **70 per cent reduction** in the number of people sleeping rough since 1998.[24]

Action plan

14. The initiatives already in place represent an important start but there is a need for more focused action if we are to tackle the serious social exclusion still faced by many adults with mental health problems. Mental health problems require more than a medical solution: they require a positive response on the part of society to accommodate people's individual needs and to promote mental well-being.

15. Our vision is of a future where people with mental health problems have the same opportunities to work and participate in the community as any other citizen. This will mean:

- communities accepting that people with mental health problems are equal;
- people receiving the support they need *before* they reach crisis point;
- people having genuine choices and a real say about what they do and the support they receive in order to fulfil their potential;
- people keeping their jobs longer and returning to employment faster, with real opportunities for career progression;
- recognition of the fundamental importance of people's relationships, family and caring responsibilities, a decent home, and participation in social and leisure activities; and
- health and social care services working in close partnership with employment and community services, with fair access regardless of ethnicity, gender, age or sexuality.

16. This report sets out a 27-point action plan to bring together the work of government departments and other organisations in a concerted effort to challenge attitudes, enable people to fulfil their aspirations, and significantly improve opportunities and outcomes for this excluded group. Action falls into six categories:

- **stigma and discrimination** – a sustained programme to challenge negative attitudes and promote awareness of people's rights;
- **the role of health and social care in tackling social exclusion** – implementing evidence-based practice in vocational services and enabling reintegration into the community;
- **employment** – giving people with mental health problems a real chance of sustained paid work reflecting their skills and experience;
- **supporting families and community participation** – enabling people to lead fulfilling lives the way they choose;
- **getting the basics right** – access to decent homes, financial advice and transport; and
- **making it happen** – clear arrangements for leading this programme and maintaining momentum.

17. There are strong links between all this work, and different parts cannot be viewed in isolation. Tackling stigma and discrimination must be a priority for all organisations and services. The advice and treatment people receive from health and social care services is critical in enabling people to fulfil their aspirations, whether this means work or other activities. Access to basic services – in particular decent housing and transport – is fundamental in enabling people to take up these opportunities.

18. The actions set out in this report aim to improve opportunities and outcomes for people with severe mental health problems, who currently have the worst social outcomes, and also for people with more common conditions who are at risk of social exclusion. This will contribute to the delivery of a number of departmental **Public Service Agreement targets**, in particular:

- the Department for Work and Pensions target to **increase the employment rate of people with disabilities, work to improve their rights and remove barriers to their participation in society**;
- the Department of Health targets to **reduce the mortality rate from suicide**, and **reduce inequalities in health outcomes**; and
- the joint Department for Work and Pensions and HM Treasury target to **halve child poverty by 2010** and **eradicate it by 2020**.

19. This report highlights the centrality of mental health to the public health agenda and the forthcoming **White Paper on improving health**. People with mental health problems have an increased risk of premature death.[25] A person with schizophrenia can expect to live for ten years less than a member of the general population,[26] and the economic costs of suicide are estimated to be in the region of £5.3 billion.[27] Mental health problems present a particular challenge for **deprived neighbourhoods**, which will be prioritised in implementing this action plan.

20. Departments have incorporated the actions set out in this report within their plans for the current financial year. For example, the new anti-stigma programme is backed by £1.1 million investment from the Department of Health. The Small Business Service has made £1.5 million available from the Phoenix Fund to be invested over two years, and the Home Office and National Institute for Mental Health in England have jointly identified up to £155,000 to strengthen police training. The Department of Health has also made available £22 million to local councils with social services responsibilities to support the capital costs associated with implementation, and has made mental health and social exclusion a funding priority for the Section 64 Grant for the voluntary sector. Investment for future years will be determined by the outcome of the current spending review.

Stigma and discrimination

21. Mental health has not benefited in recent decades from the progress seen in tackling stigma and discrimination in areas such as sexuality and race. A reinforced drive is needed, drawing on international evidence of what works, through:

- a sustained programme backed by £1.1 million investment in 2004-05 to challenge discrimination against people with mental health problems, with closer co-ordination across government and the voluntary sector;
- practical teaching resources to challenge the stigma surrounding mental health from an early age through schools; and
- planning for vigorous implementation of the proposed new public sector duty to promote equality of opportunity for disabled people.

The role of health and social care services in tackling social exclusion

22. The advice that people with mental health problems receive from health and social care professionals can set the tone for the course of their illness and its impact on their lives. Support for reintegration into the community is an integral part of the work of effective mental health services. Early access to mental health services regardless of age, ethnicity, gender or social status may reduce the risk of problems becoming more intractable. Health and social care services will tackle social exclusion through:

- modernised vocational services which reflect evidence-based practice and provide a choice of services to meet diverse needs;
- access to an employment adviser and social support for everyone with severe mental health problems;
- redesigning mental health day services to promote social inclusion;
- improved access to vocational and social support in primary care;
- strengthened training on social inclusion for health and social care professionals;
- measures to tackle inequalities in access to health services; and
- closer working with the criminal justice system, including strengthened police training on mental health issues.

Employment

23. Large numbers of adults with mental health problems want to work, and employment promotes improved mental health. The *Pathways to Work* pilots are testing the impact of a comprehensive employment support package including specialist personal advisers, help for people to manage their condition better in a work environment, and better financial incentives through the £40 per week return to work credit. In addition, people with mental health problems will be better supported to find and retain work through:

- improved training on mental health issues for Jobcentre Plus staff;
- £1.5 million from the Phoenix Fund to improve support for adults with mental health problems who are interested in enterprise and self-employment;
- clearer guidance on the use of *Access to Work* to fund adjustments for this client group, and on the continuing needs of Disability Living Allowance claimants upon returning to work;
- consideration of further improvements to the linking rules and permitted work rules to support the transition from benefits to work; and
- improved support for employers and job retention through the government's new vocational rehabilitation framework.

Supporting families and community participation

24. Mental health problems do not just affect individuals but also their family and friends. Providing early support to families can help to prevent children's longer-term emotional and mental health problems. Early recognition of mental health problems in parents, especially around birth, and provision of support can also help prevent their mental health problems from developing further.

25. Local services such as colleges, arts and sports activities offer opportunities to meet people from outside mental health services and integrate into the community. This report's action plan supports people's right to participate fully in society through:

- improved support to access education and training opportunities;
- a strengthened evidence base to enable wider roll-out of arts interventions;
- targeted family support to meet the needs of the many parents with mental health problems and their children; and
- removal of unnecessary barriers to community roles such as jury service, and more consistent practice on paying people with experience of mental health problems to advise on service design.

Getting the basics right

26. There is little prospect of accessing work or community activities for people whose housing is unstable, who have problems with money and who are unable to access affordable transport. The action plan addresses these issues through:

- new guidance to housing authorities on lettings and stability for adults with mental health problems; and
- improved access to financial and legal advice, and affordable transport.

Making it happen

27. To ensure that this action plan is implemented and followed through requires effective leadership and co-ordination at national and local level. This will be achieved through:

- a cross-government team tasked with driving implementation, with progress overseen by ministers;
- an independent advisory group to advise the government on progress;
- local implementation led jointly by primary care trusts and local authorities, supported by the National Institute for Mental Health in England; and
- better use of the expertise in the voluntary and community sector.

Conclusion

28. This report marks the start of a sustained programme of change to challenge discriminatory attitudes and significantly improve opportunities and outcomes for adults with mental health problems. This will mean people with mental health problems regaining hope and recovering control of their lives, whatever their diagnosis or ongoing symptoms. Government has an important role to play, but the active involvement of the voluntary and community sector, employers and, crucially, people with personal experience of mental health problems will be essential to achieve real change.

29. The report features case studies of many successful local projects and the experiences of individuals who have overcome the challenges posed by mental health problems to lead fulfilling lives. These examples demonstrate what can be achieved and the benefits that result for individuals and society.

Ude's story – help to find employment

Ude had been in prison and had spells in hospital with severe mental health problems. He was referred to the First Step Trust in Lambeth, which provides work projects for people with mental health problems and other disabilities or disadvantages. At First Step Trust, Ude discovered that he had a flair for organising people and managing small teams of workers on site and in the community. He has recently been appointed to a salaried position and manages the gardening section, which is the project's largest commercial contract with an annual income of £90,000. *"I had to get my life together,"* says Ude, *"and I did it through work."* Today he lives in his own flat in the community and has minimal contact with mental health support services.

CHAPTER 1: What is the problem and why does it matter?

Summary

- Only 24 per cent of adults with long-term mental health problems are in work, and too many spend their time inactive and alone.
- Mental health problems are estimated to cost over £77 billion per year through care costs, economic losses and premature death. Earlier intervention to keep people in work and maintain social contacts could significantly reduce these costs.
- Severe mental health problems are relatively rare, and strongly associated with poor social outcomes. Depression and anxiety are more common, with the highest rates found among socially disadvantaged groups.

"Everyone should have the opportunity to have a family, to work, to live."

"It's about people who happen to use mental health services being treated as people."

What do we mean by 'mental health problems'?

In this report, we have grouped mental health problems in two main categories:

- **severe and enduring mental health problems** including psychotic disorders (schizophrenia and bipolar affective disorder, also known as manic depression). An estimated one in 200 adults had a psychotic disorder in the past year, and about one in 25 adults had a personality disorder;[28] and
- **common mental health problems** such as anxiety, depression, phobias, obsessive-compulsive and panic disorders. An estimated one in six people has common mental health problems at any one time.[29]

The impact of mental health problems

1. Mental health problems can be both a cause and a consequence of social exclusion. Anyone can be affected by mental health problems, but people from deprived backgrounds are at significantly greater risk. Some people might need to take a few weeks off work but otherwise carry on as before. For others, mental health problems can spark off a chain of events, such as loss of employment leading to debt, housing problems and relationship breakdown. This can in turn contribute to worsening mental health.

- **Only 24 per cent** of adults with long-term mental health problems are **in work** – the lowest employment rate for any of the main groups of disabled people.[30]
- People with mental health problems are at **more than double** the risk of **losing their job** than those without.[31]

- Many people experience their **first episode** of mental health problems in their **late teens or early twenties**, which can have serious consequences for their education and employment prospects.[32]
- Two-thirds of men under the age of 35 with mental health problems who die by **suicide** are unemployed.[33]
- People with mental health problems are nearly **three times** more likely to be in **debt**.[34]
- **One in four** tenants with mental health problems has serious **rent arrears** and is at risk of losing his or her home.[35]
- People with a severe mental health problem are **three times** more likely to be **divorced** than those without.[36]

Victoria's story – breaking the cycle of social exclusion

Victoria had a variety of successful but stressful jobs and coped with the stress by harming herself. She became agoraphobic and started using cocaine to give her courage to leave the house. Scared of the psychiatric system, she refused help until she was in a crisis. While in hospital, she was evicted from her flat and was then discharged to a hostel where she lived for seven months while waiting for council housing. For the first time she relied on benefits, but not only was she too ashamed to ask for advice, she didn't know where to find it. She used her Incapacity Benefit to pay council tax, not knowing that she was entitled to Council Tax Benefit or that she could apply for Disability Living Allowance.

Victoria's debts mounted and she received a court summons, making her even more anxious and depressed. She was referred to the Cawley Centre, a therapeutic community in London, where she received intensive psychotherapy as well as practical and emotional support. A welfare adviser helped her claim the correct benefits and negotiate a repayment plan with creditors, and an occupational therapist went with her to make the payments. A weekly 'Future Prospects' group encouraged her to start going out on her own, and a volunteer group called Sabre encouraged her to start thinking about a future career and advised her about permitted work rules. She now volunteers as a classroom assistant at a local primary school for two mornings a week and attends evening classes once a week.

"I spent years in a cycle of hospital admissions because of suicide attempts and self-harm, and I didn't believe that could change. It took more than just therapy – it took practical support and the right advice and encouragement – to show me the future really can be different. I owe my life to the Cawley Centre."

The economic cost

2. The Sainsbury Centre for Mental Health has estimated the annual costs of mental health problems in England to be £77.4 billion.[37] The impact on quality of life, including premature mortality, accounted for well over half that figure. Output losses associated with missed employment opportunities were estimated at over £23 billion per year. State benefits to adults with mental health problems were estimated at £9.5 billion.[38]

Figure 1: Total cost of mental health problems, England 2002-03

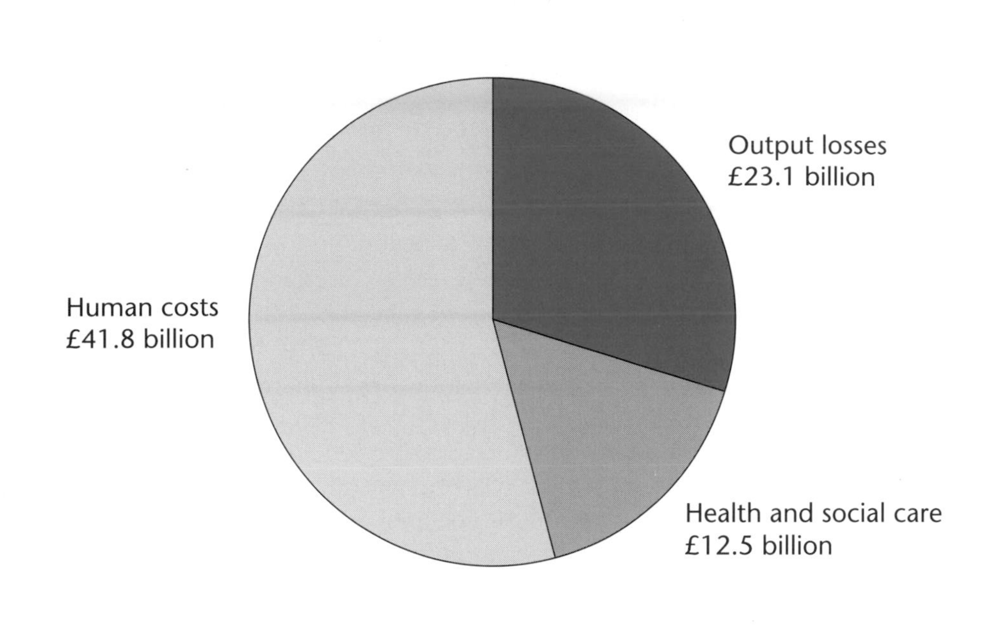

Source: The Sainsbury Centre for Mental Health, *Policy Paper 3: The economic and social costs of mental illness,* (London, The Sainsbury Centre for Mental Health, 2003).

3. In 2002, over 32 million prescription items were dispensed in the community for the treatment of mental health problems, costing over £540 million.[39] Failure to prevent mental health problems leading to social exclusion can trigger a range of social and financial costs, as illustrated in Annex B.

4. Mental health problems can also lead to personal debt and financial problems. Adults with severe and enduring mental health problems are over five times, and those with common mental health problems over three times more likely to cut down on use of the telephone, gas, electricity and water than the general population.[40]

Who is affected by mental health problems?

5. The Office for National Statistics (ONS) *Psychiatric Morbidity Survey (2000)* estimated that about **one in every 200** adults in the general population had experienced 'probable **psychotic disorder**' in the past year,[41] and about **one in 25** adults had a **personality disorder**.[42] An estimated one in 100 of the population will have schizophrenia at some point in their lifetime and similar numbers will experience bipolar affective disorder during their lives.[43]

6. The ONS estimated that around **one in six** of the general population has **common mental health problems** at any one time.[44] One in ten **new mothers** is estimated to experience **post-natal depression**.[45] Overall, the ONS estimate that there has been no significant change in the prevalence of mental health problems over the last decade, except a slight increase in neurotic disorders among men.[46] However, depression is projected by the World Health Organisation to become the leading cause of disability and the second leading contributor to the global burden of disease by the year 2020.[47] Among young people, there have been substantial increases in psychosocial disorders since the 1940s in nearly all developed countries.[48]

7. **Over 900,000** adults in England claiming **sickness and disability benefits** (Incapacity Benefit or Severe Disablement Allowance[49]) report mental health problems as their primary condition, almost twice as many as in 1995.[50] Possible explanations for this increase include:

   - a diagnosis of mental health problems has become more acceptable for GPs and patients as stress and anxiety are more openly discussed;[51]

   - changes in the labour market could mean that mental health has become a more important factor in retaining employment than physical health; and

   - increased job insecurity coupled with higher expectations at work.[52]

8. The impact of mental health problems **over time** varies significantly. About half of people with common mental health problems are no longer affected after 18 months, but people of lower socio-economic status, the long-term sick and unemployed are more likely still to be affected.[53] More severe episodes of depression typically last between three to nine months, with a high risk of recurrence. Around a quarter of people (1,500 people) who die by suicide in the UK had been in contact with mental health services in the year before their death.[54]

9. Approximately one-quarter of people with schizophrenia will make a good recovery with some form of treatment within five years, two-thirds will experience multiple episodes with some degree of disability, and between one in ten and one in six will develop severe long-term disabilities.[55] One-fifth of people affected by bipolar disorder will only have one episode.

10. Although severe mental health problems can be especially disabling, common mental health problems can also have a major impact on people's lives.[56] Further analysis of the *Psychiatric Morbidity Survey (1993)* has suggested that about half of people with common mental health problems are limited by their condition and around a fifth are disabled by it.[57]

11. As **Figure 2** shows, certain groups of people are at **high risk** for common mental health problems, including those with less education or who are unemployed.[58] Chronic physical ill health and adverse life events, such as bereavement or moving home, also increase the risk.[59]

Figure 2: High-risk subgroups as a percentage of the general population aged 16-64, and the prevalence of neurotic disorder in each group (note: group membership overlaps)

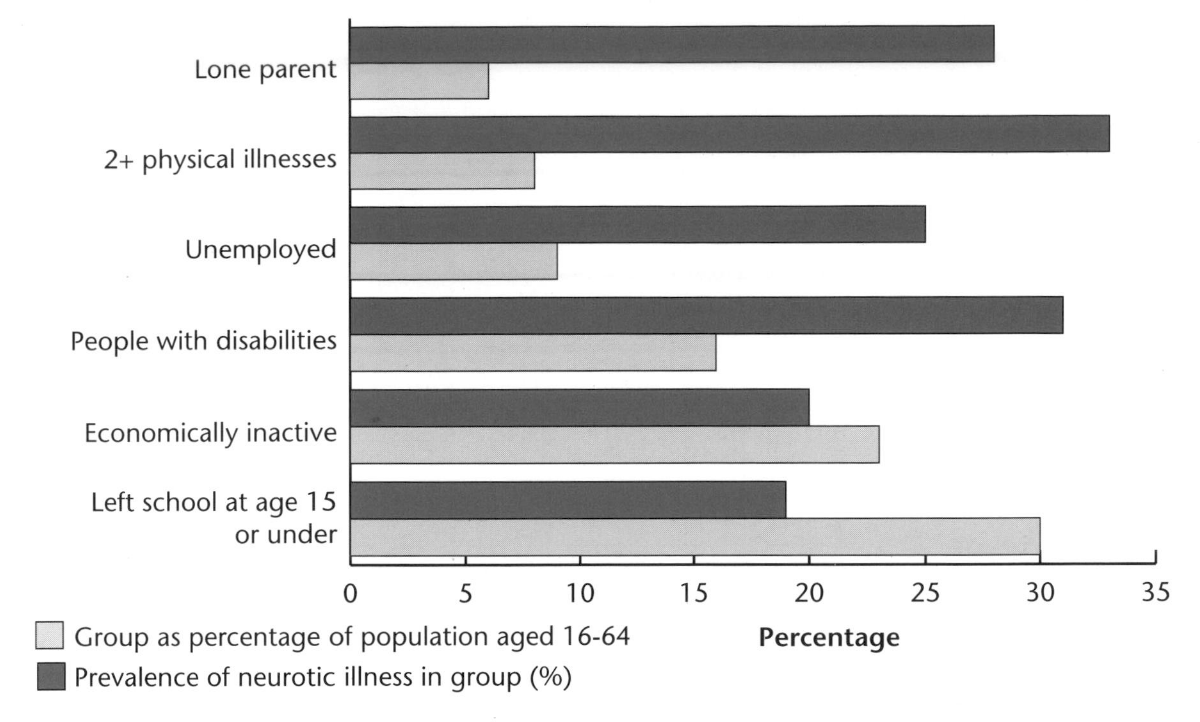

Source: D Melzer, T Fryers and R Jenkins (Eds) *Social Inequalities and the Distribution of the Common Mental Disorders, Maudsley Monograph 44*, (Hove, Psychology Press, 2004).

12. Prevalence and successful diagnosis of mental health problems can vary according to a range of factors.

- **Age:** the average age of onset of psychotic symptoms is 22.[60] Up to half of all adult mental health problems begin in childhood.[61] Common mental health problems peak for men aged 45-49 years and for women from 50-54 years.[62]

- **Gender:** women have higher rates of common mental health problems than men,[63] and are more likely to experience longer-term episodes of depression, with greater likelihood of recurrence. Young men aged 25-34 are a particularly high risk group for suicide.[64]

Figure 3: Common mental health problems by age and sex

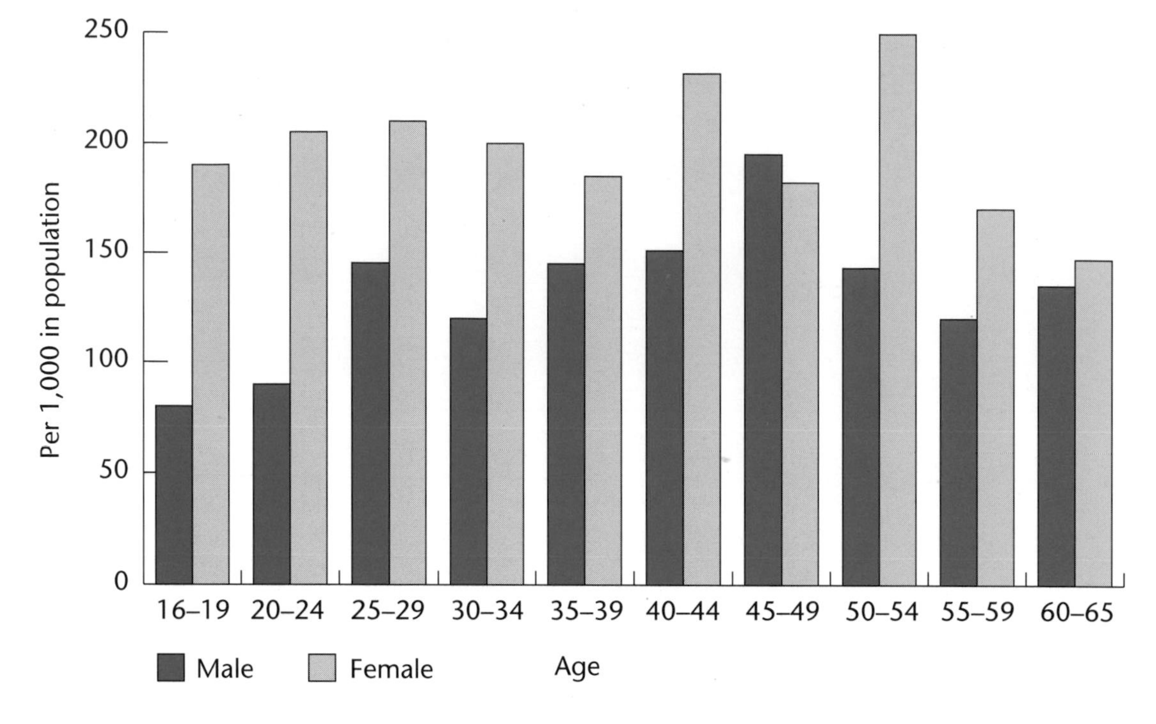

Data source: Office for National Statistics *2000 Psychiatric Morbidity Survey.*

- **Ethnicity:** people from ethnic minority groups are six times more likely to be detained under the Mental Health Act than white people.[65] Rates of diagnosed psychotic disorders are estimated twice as high among African Caribbean people than white people,[66] although they are three to five times more likely to be diagnosed and admitted to hospital for schizophrenia.[67] South Asian women born in India and East Africa have a 40 per cent higher suicide rate than those born in England and Wales.[68] The prevalence of common mental health problems is fairly similar across different ethnic groups, although rates are higher for Irish men and Pakistani women and lower for Bangladeshi women.[69]

Chinese Outreach Service, the Kinhon Project, Sheffield

The four primary care trusts in Sheffield provide an outreach service to their Chinese population, as members of the community are often reluctant to access mainstream services, and half cannot speak English. The project provides a women's drop-in centre and advocacy/translation services, and helps identify high-risk groups. They would like to expand to provide more accessible drop-in facilities, a telephone helpline and an outreach worker for men.

- **Parents and carers:** 20-50 per cent of adults using adult mental health services are parents. An estimated 28 per cent of lone parents have common mental health problems.[70] Black Caribbean children have a 50 per cent chance of being born to a lone parent,[71] and Caribbean single mothers have higher rates of severe and enduring mental health problems than married women (but similar rates of common mental health problems).[72] Up to 420,000 people in the UK care for someone with a mental health problem,[73] including 6,000 to 17,000 young carers.[74] Carers are twice as likely to have mental health problems themselves if they provide substantial care.[75]

- **Occupation:** in 2001-02, around half a million people believed work-related stress was making them ill.[76] Teachers, nurses and managers are most likely to report high levels of stress.[77] People working in the medical and farming professions are at greatest risk of suicide.[78] One in five firefighters,[79] and around one in seven young people in the armed forces with significant combat experience,[80] is likely to suffer from post-traumatic stress disorder. A minority of ex-armed forces personnel have problems adapting to life outside the services, and may be significantly over-represented in prison, and in the homeless and rough sleeping populations.

Figure 4: High work stress by occupation

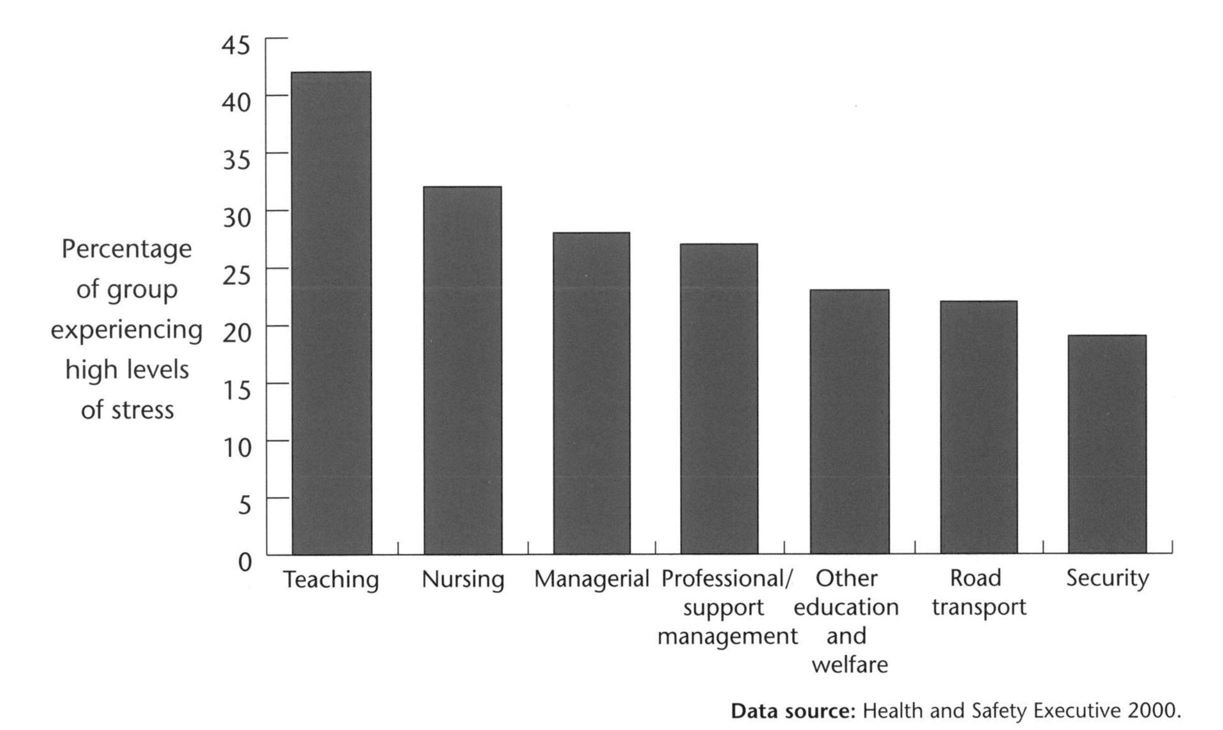

Data source: Health and Safety Executive 2000.

GP services, North Northumberland

North Northumberland has a GP leading on mental health issues across the region. The GP acts as a 'supervisor' for a group of eight professional carers (both GPs and nurses) for a contracted monthly confidential session to share and manage their concerns. The aim of the group is to reduce their stress and promote their well-being. The GP is also available on an informal basis for staff in the primary health care team and in the two local cottage hospitals in the area to discuss any mental health problems in confidence.

- **Location:** deprived areas and remote rural districts have the highest levels of mental health problems and suicide.[81,82] Suicide rates in the North West are significantly higher than in England and Wales as a whole.

Figure 5: Prevalence of mental health problems by region

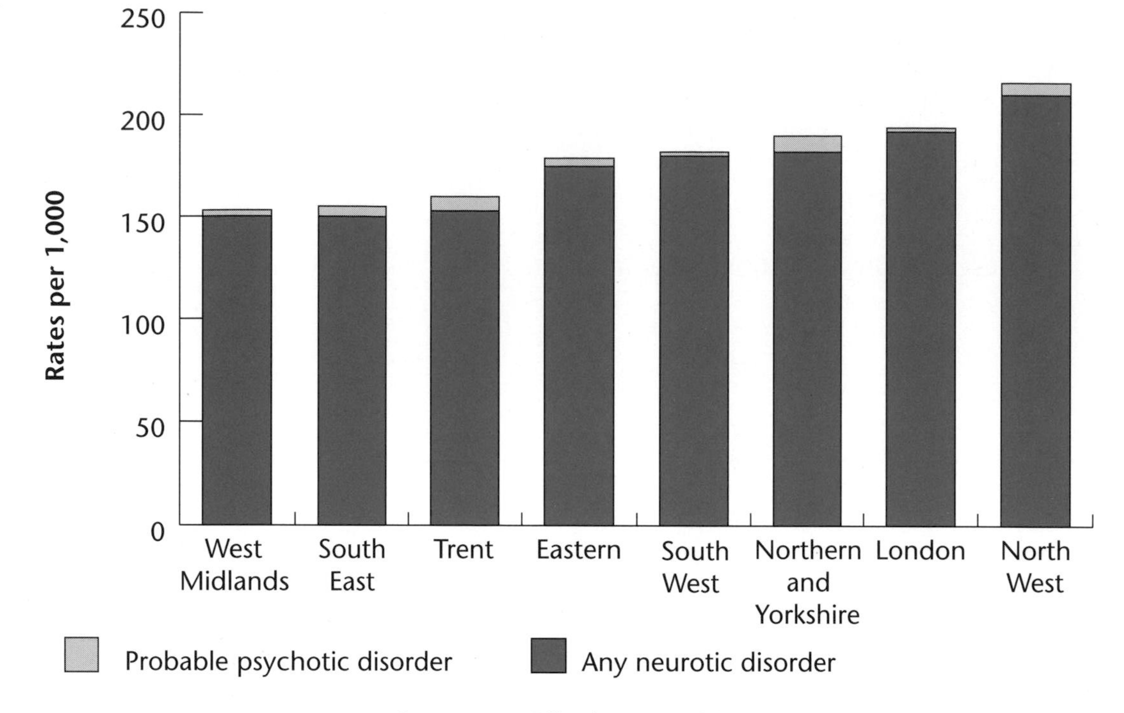

Data source: Office for National Statistics *2000 Psychiatric Morbidity Survey.*

- **Victims of abuse:** mental health problems are often experienced by adult victims of domestic violence and those who have been sexually abused in childhood.[83]

13. The Social Exclusion Unit has identified a number of groups with **complex needs** at particular risk of mental health problems and social exclusion who may struggle to have their needs met through statutory agencies.

- Approximately 30-50 per cent of people misusing **drugs** have mental health problems.[84] In one study, half of **alcohol** dependent adults said they had a mental health problem.[85] Rates of co-morbidity of drug and alcohol use and psychiatric problems are believed to be rising.[86]

- 72 per cent of male and 70 per cent of female sentenced **prisoners** have two or more mental health disorders: 14 and 35 times the level in the general population respectively.[87] Prevalence rates for psychotic disorders are also high, especially for female prisoners.[88] 20 per cent of male and 37 per cent of female sentenced prisoners have attempted suicide.[89] Between 2002 and 2003, there were 105 suicides in prison.[90]

- Suicide accounts for one in four deaths of **homeless** people.[91] Studies have consistently shown that between 30 and 50 per cent of rough sleepers have mental health problems.[92,93]

- Two-thirds of **refugees** have experienced anxiety or depression.[94] They might have faced war, imprisonment, torture or oppression in their home country. In their new country, they can experience additional factors linked to poor mental health,[95] including social isolation, homelessness, language difficulties, and racial discrimination.[96] Migrants have higher rates of severe mental health problems. Rates of psychosis among white people migrating to predominantly white communities are twice as high as the general population, and four times as high among black people migrating to predominantly white communities.[97]

- An estimated 25-40 per cent of people with **learning disabilities** experience risk factors associated with mental health problems.[98] Approximately 30 per cent of **deaf people** using British Sign Language have mental health problems, primarily mood and anxiety disorders.[99] At March 2000, 3.5 per cent of registered **blind people** also had mental health problems.[100]

Preventing social exclusion

Mental health problems do not have to trigger social exclusion. With early intervention and effective support, many more people can retain their jobs and social contacts. In the chapters that follow, this report sets out the main causes of social exclusion among adults with mental health problems, and identifies action to tackle these problems.

CHAPTER 2: Breaking the cycle

Summary

- Mental health problems can lead to a vicious cycle of social exclusion, including unemployment, debt, homelessness and worsening health. With the right support this cycle can be broken.
- Underlying causes of social exclusion include stigma and discrimination, unclear responsibilities and a lack of co-ordination between agencies, a narrow focus on medical symptoms, and limited support to return to work.
- Breaking the cycle requires a focus on early intervention, and fulfilling people's aspirations and potential through work and social participation.

"Mental ill health does contribute to social exclusion because it affects your confidence to participate in the life of your community."

1. Chapter 1 considered the impact and prevalence of mental health problems. This chapter looks at how mental health problems can trigger a long-term cycle of exclusion for individuals, and how this negative cycle can be broken.

A cycle of exclusion

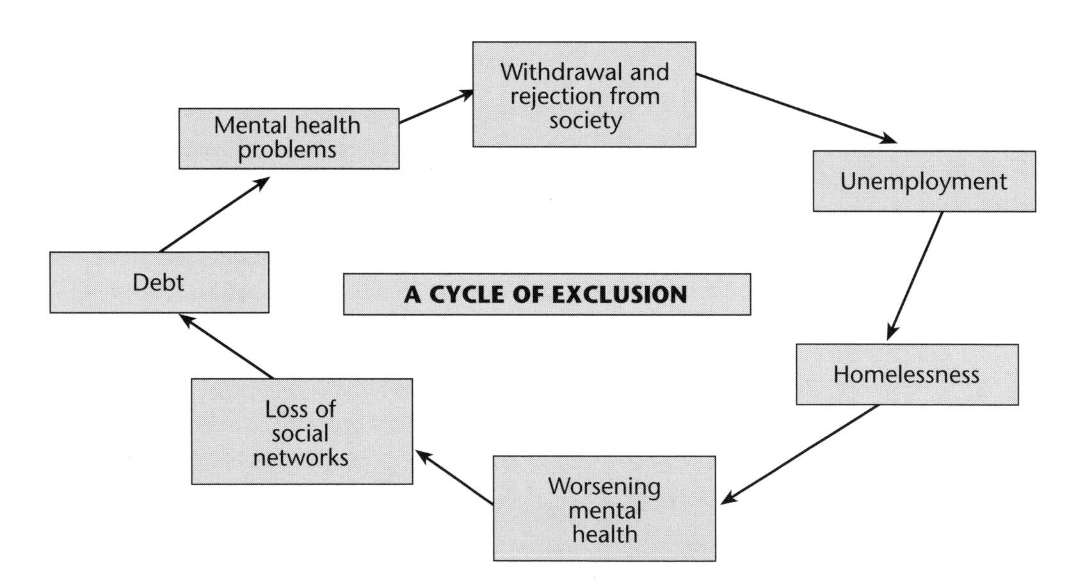

2. Even a short episode of mental health problems can have a long-term impact on a person's life, relationships and employment opportunities. A single hospital admission or period of sickness absence from work can lead to unemployment, homelessness, debt and social isolation. This can in turn lead to worsening mental health and a cycle of exclusion. As well as affecting the individual, mental health problems can also have a wider impact on children and families.

3. Early intervention to keep people in work and maintain their social support can prevent this cycle from developing. Even at a later stage, with the right support, the cycle can be broken.

Darren's story – the importance of specialist intervention

After being made unemployed at 19, Darren became depressed and got into trouble with the police. His mum threw him out of the house because of his behaviour, and for seven months he slept rough, becoming more depressed. He couldn't see a way out.

He was helped to find accommodation, but remained depressed, and was drinking alcohol and smoking cannabis. He started feeling suicidal after four people in his family died. His probation officer suggested that he contact Antenna, a voluntary organisation that supports young African-Caribbean people with mental health problems. Darren started going to Antenna almost every day. He says it saved his life and helped him realise he was ill with depression. In the past few years, he has found permanent housing, is now married with a daughter, and is studying at university.

Why does it happen?

4. The underlying causes of the social exclusion experienced by many adults with mental health problems include:

- **stigma and discrimination**, actual or fear of rejection from the community leading to people wanting to stay in the safety of mental health services rather than engaging in the mainstream;
- a **lack of clear responsibility** for improving vocational and social outcomes for adults with mental health problems;
- different services not always **working effectively** together to meet individual needs and maximise the impact of available resources;
- **diagnoses** of mental health problems being missed or inaccurate, and a focus on **medical symptoms** rather than social and vocational roles;
- professionals not having the **time, training or local contacts** to help people move into work or participate in their local communities; and
- a **lack of support** to enable people **to work**, with fears about leaving benefits and employers not knowing where to go for help.

Liz's story – overcoming stigma and discrimination

Liz worked as a journalist but experienced severe bouts of depression. She was worried about anyone finding out about her mental health problem, and stopped seeing her doctor because she didn't want to take time off work. She would explain occasional manic episodes as simply working too hard.

Liz was eventually hospitalised several times. When she tried to go back to work, she couldn't get a job interview because of her mental health history. This triggered serious depression and she was detained under the Mental Health Act, and later became homeless. While recovering she started to use her skills in the mental health field – writing, training journalists, speaking to the media and consulting with the voluntary sector. In 2002, she received the Mental Health Media Survivor Award. She joined the Social Exclusion Unit's mental health team in 2003 and is helping to set up the National Institute for Mental Health in England's programme to tackle stigma and discrimination.

While she still experiences symptoms of manic depression, she has learned to cope with the support of occupational therapists and a psychologist, as well as a supportive GP and regular appointments with psychiatrists.

"Just two years ago I felt my life was over. I couldn't see any way of getting back to how I used to be, and I felt useless. Being back at work, having a secure home and having the confidence to see my friends again has transformed my life. And I know that support is there when I need it – at work, from my psychologist and from my friends and family."

How to break the cycle

"People whose symptoms continue or recur can and do live satisfying lives, and contribute to their communities in many different ways, [but] the alleviation of such symptoms does not necessarily result in the reinstatement of former, valued roles and relationships." [101]

5. People with mental health problems can regain the things they value in life regardless of their diagnosis or symptoms. This requires more than medical treatment, it requires a positive response from society to accommodate individual needs and differing contributions.[102] There are a number of building blocks needed to promote social inclusion.

- **Inclusive communities:** a reduction of stigma and discrimination within the local community to support reintegration and the acceptance of people with mental health problems as equal citizens.
- **Early intervention:** offering support and help before people reach crisis point in a way that is non-stigmatising and easily accessible.
- **Empowerment and the right to individual choice:** breaking the perceived link between mental health problems and incompetence, to provide individuals with control over their own care and future.
- **A focus on employment:** recognition that jobs provide a sense of worth and identity as well as financial security. Working is associated with better health outcomes and reduced need for health and other services.
- **Promoting broader social participation:** education, training or volunteering, particularly in mainstream settings, can increase employment prospects as well as being valuable in their own right. They can help build self-confidence and social networks, as can sports and arts activities. Sports can help improve people's physical as well as mental health.

- **Securing basic entitlements:** decent housing, basic financial and transport services, and ensuring people are aware of their rights.
- **Acknowledging people's social networks and family relationships:** recognising the central role that family members and friends can play in reintegration into communities.
- **Building confidence and trust:** making services more welcoming and promoting understanding of different needs to encourage people who may mistrust statutory services, such as some ethnic minorities or parents, to engage with services earlier.

6. This report sets out a new vision for partnership working across sectors and an action plan to achieve change (see Chapter 9). Health and social care services have a critical role to play in helping people recover what they value in life, by facilitating access to advice and support and addressing inequalities in access to health care. There needs to be stronger links between health, social care and employment opportunities, and improvements in employment support. More opportunities for social participation need to be developed, with better access to education, volunteering and leisure. Providing the basics of housing, financial stability and better transport will enable people with mental health problems to take full advantage of these opportunities. Stigma and discrimination must be addressed in every area of life.

A framework for change

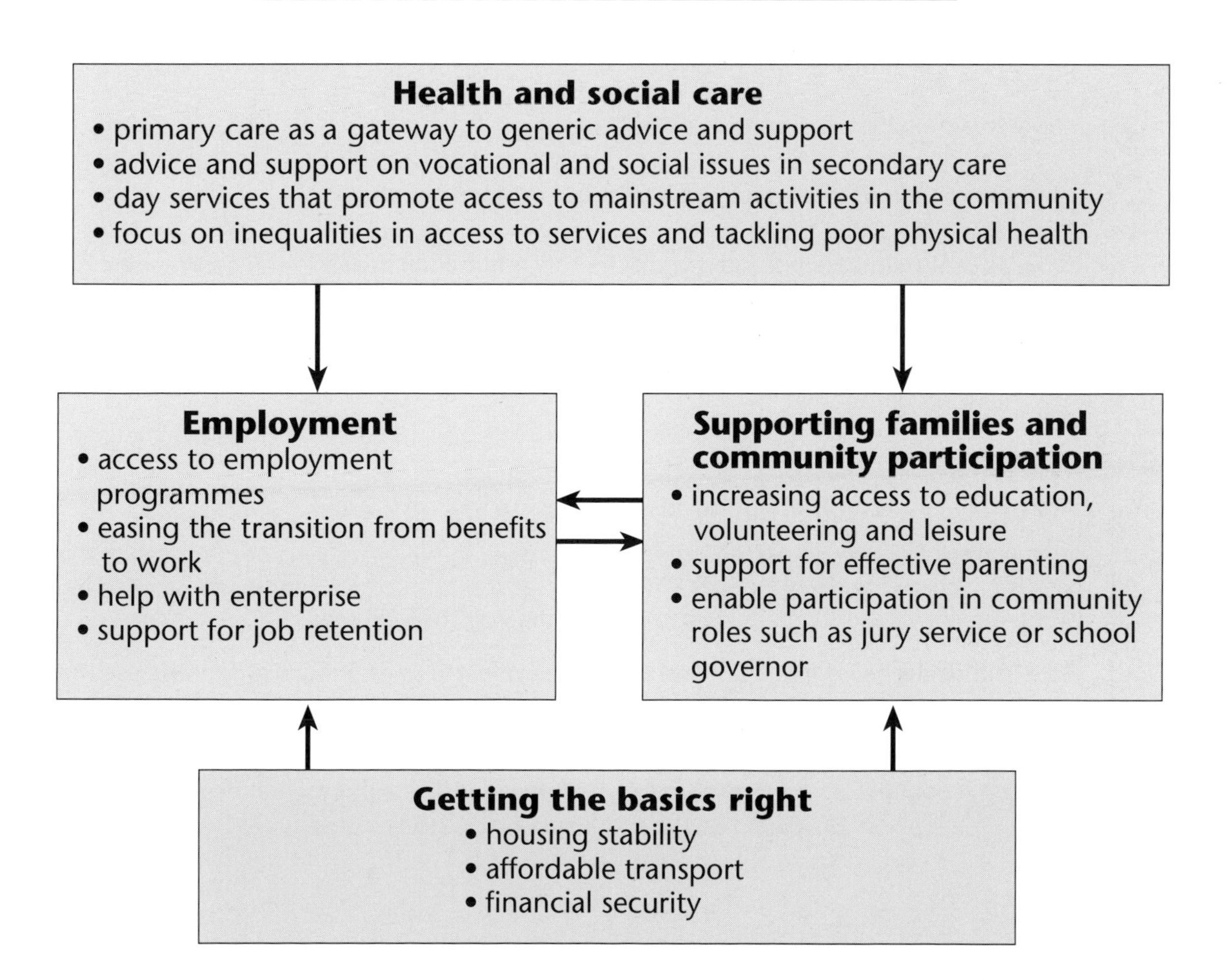

CHAPTER 3: Stigma and discrimination

Summary

- Over 80 per cent of respondents to the Social Exclusion Unit consultation said that tackling stigma and discrimination was a priority.
- Stigma and discrimination limits people's aspirations and can make it difficult for them to work, access services, participate in communities and enjoy family life.
- Previous campaigns to tackle stigma have had mixed success. International evidence indicates that sustained work to challenge discrimination is the best way to achieve behavioural change.
- The Disability Discrimination Act 1995 outlawed discrimination against disabled people, but people with mental health problems, employers and service providers may have poor awareness of the protection provided by this legislation.

The impact of stigma and discrimination

> *"I feel reluctant to admit I've got mental health problems; the stigma and rejection are too hard to face."*[103]

1. The greatest barriers to social inclusion for people with mental health problems are stigma and the resulting discrimination. Respondents to the Social Exclusion Unit consultation said that prejudice and lack of understanding make it difficult for people to work, access health services, participate in their communities, and enjoy family life. Although the consultation did not specifically ask about stigma:

- 83 per cent identified stigma as a key issue;
- 55 per cent identified stigma as a barrier to employment; and
- 52 per cent mentioned negative attitudes towards mental health in the community.

2. Stigma and discrimination can affect people long after the symptoms of mental health problems have been resolved. Discrimination can lead to relapses in mental health problems and can intensify existing symptoms.[104]

What do we mean by stigma, discrimination and prejudice?

Stigma arises from negative stereotypes associated with the symptoms or diagnosis of mental health problems. Although stigma is often seen as the problem of people with mental health problems, they can lack the power to change the way they are seen.

Discrimination is being treated unfairly or denied opportunities. Programmes to tackle mental health stigma have begun to place more emphasis on discrimination, addressing society's response rather than placing the onus on people with a history of mental health problems.[105]

Prejudice is public fear, misunderstanding and intolerance around mental health issues.

3. Despite national action to tackle stigma and discrimination, public attitudes towards mental health are not improving. In 1993, 92 per cent of people agreed that *"we need to adopt a far more tolerant attitude toward people with mental illness in our society"*, but this had dropped to 83 per cent in 2003. [106]

Sanity Fair, Stoke-on-Trent

Sanity Fair is an annual weekend carnival aiming to reduce stigma in a fun way. Entertainers attract people to stalls with information on mental health issues and available services. Local press reports estimated 20,000 people attended in 2003. Sanity Fair is organised by people who have experienced mental health problems, with support from the local authority and the *Give it Sum* charity.

Loss of confidence

"I have tremendous difficulty in seeing myself both as a competent researcher and as someone who has experienced mental health problems. Sometimes it is as though the two images of myself cannot co-exist: as one comes into focus, the other fades and becomes indistinct." [107]

4. Fear of stigma and discrimination can lead to severe loss of confidence or 'self stigma'.[108] This can lead to social exclusion, causing people to withdraw from social activities and friendships, and give up applying for jobs even when they are free of the symptoms of mental ill health. Approximately three-quarters of respondents in a recent Mind survey felt that lack of understanding by others about mental health issues was a key cause of isolation.[109]

Myths about adults with mental health problems

"I'm a good deal safer sitting on a train next to someone with schizophrenia than I am standing outside a city centre pub at 11 o'clock on a Saturday night." [110]

Myth one: *they are dangerous and violent*. Less than 5 per cent of people who kill a stranger have symptoms of mental illness.[111] For every one person killed by someone with a mental health problem there are 70 deaths on the roads.[112] People with mental health problems are more likely to be victims than perpetrators of violence: a study of people with psychosis in British inner-city areas reported that 16 per cent had been the victims of violence, compared with about 7 per cent of the inner-city population overall.[113]

Myth two: *they can't work*. A large proportion of people with mental health problems, including those with severe conditions, can gain and retain employment if they have the right kind of support on an ongoing basis.[114] US research found that up to 58 per cent of adults with severe and enduring mental health problems are able to work with the right support.[115]

Myth three: *they don't want to work*. 35 per cent of people with mental health problems are economically inactive but would like to work (compared to 28 per cent with other health problems).[116]

Myth four: *they are incapable of making their own decisions*. Many successful business people, professionals, politicians and scientists have had mental health problems.

Myth five: *mental health problems are rare and unusual*. Common mental health problems affect up to 16 per cent of the general population at any one time.[117]

Figure 6: Homicides and mental illness, England and Wales

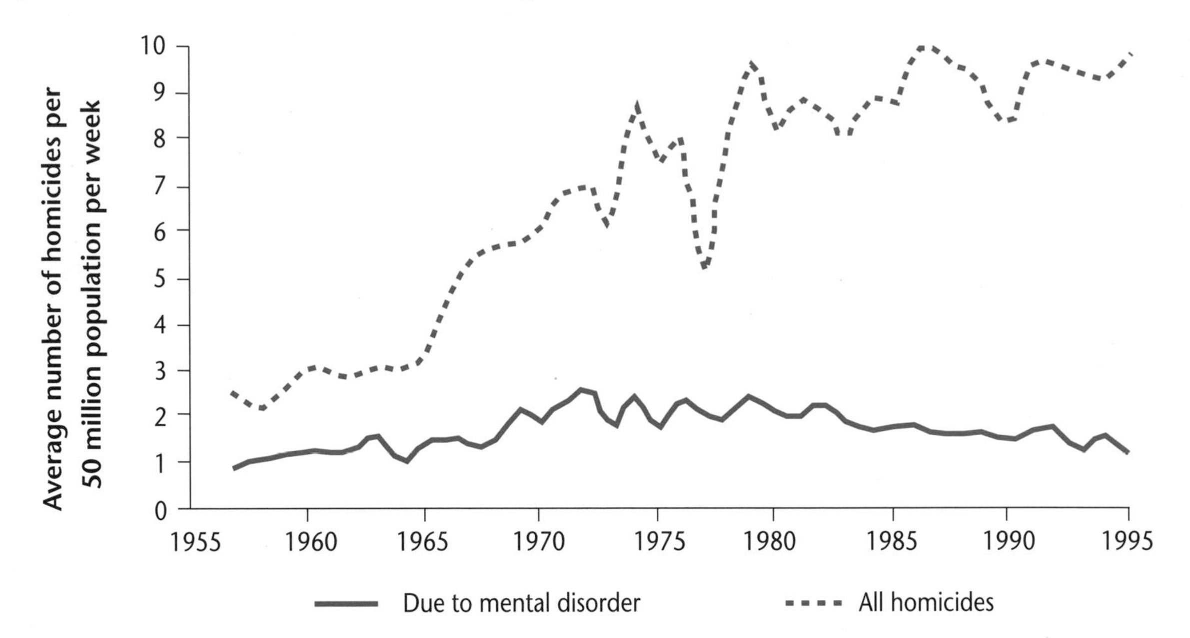

Source: P Taylor and J Gunn, 'Homicides by people with mental illness', *British Journal of Psychiatry*, 174 (1999).

The media and associations with violence

> *"Acquaintances who have no experience of mental health take any knowledge from the media, and then laugh and are disrespectful. I find my mental health problems are my best kept secret because even close friends and family have been influenced by the media."*[118]

5. The proportion of people with mental health problems likely to display violent behaviour is small. People with severe mental health problems are more likely to be victims of violence. However, the media strongly associates mental health problems with violence, and reporting can be inaccurate and out of perspective.[119]

6. Two-thirds of all British press and television coverage on mental health includes an association with violence.[120] A study of tabloid media found that 40 per cent of daily tabloid articles and nearly half of Sunday tabloid articles about mental health contained derogatory terms such as 'nutter' and 'loony'.[121] Research on attitudes amongst the British adult population has found that *"...people with mental illness, particularly people with schizophrenia or addictions, are viewed as dangerous and unpredictable."*[122]

7. International research has found that people who received their information from the electronic media are less tolerant of people with mental health problems than those who received it from other sources.[123] A study in New Zealand found that children's television contains frequent derogatory language and portrayal of mental health.[124]

8. There has been little monitoring of the portrayal of mental health problems on British television, but *Counting the Cost* analysed the effects of media portrayals on people with mental health problems:[125]

- 50 per cent said that it had a negative effect on their mental health;
- 33 per cent felt reluctant to apply for jobs or to volunteer; and
- 37 per cent said their families or friends reacted differently to them because of recent media coverage.

Employment

"We're not accepted when we go back to work, no matter that you can do the job. They don't treat you as an equal, they're always a bit wary." [126]

"[I was] forced by occupational health to forfeit [an] appointment as Finance Director because of manic depression." [127]

Figure 7: Percentage of employers who would recruit from different groups

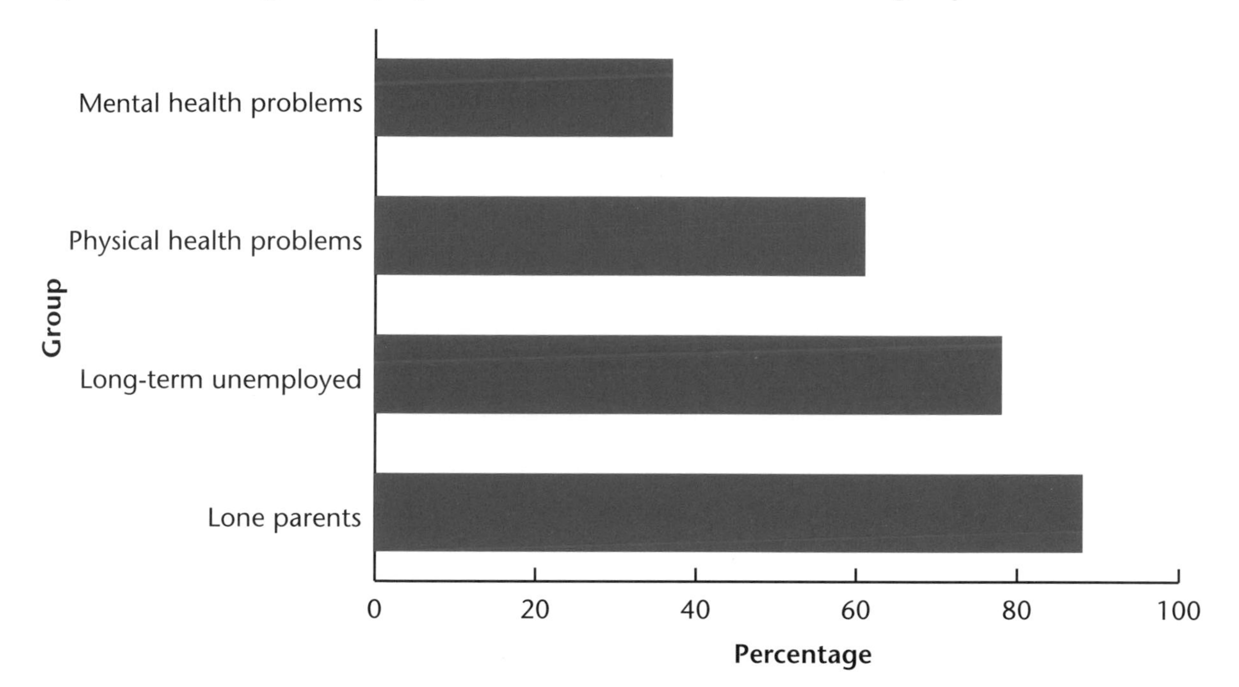

Data source: ONE Evaluation: Department for Work and Pensions, 2001

9. Stigma and discrimination, both realised and perceived, are major barriers to employment. Fewer than four in ten employers would consider employing someone with a history of mental health problems, compared to more than six in ten for physical disability.[128] Three-quarters of employers believe that it would be difficult or impossible to employ someone with schizophrenia, even though schizophrenia can be controlled with medication and would not require physical adaptations to the work environment.[129] Some staff interviewed for the research expressed concerns because of the perceived link to violence. In another study, 200 personnel managers were asked to assess the employment prospects of two job applicants who were identical save that one was diagnosed with diabetes and the other with depression.[130] The applicant with depression had significantly reduced chances of employment.

10. One-third of people with mental health problems report having been dismissed or forced to resign from their job.[131] Almost four in ten felt they had been denied a job because of their previous psychiatric history,[132] and over two-thirds had been put off applying for jobs for fear of unfair treatment.[133]

11. There is anecdotal evidence of some employment contracts including within their definition of gross misconduct, which would trigger instant dismissal, clauses such as *"if you become of unsound mind or a patient under the Mental Health Act 1983."*

Health services

"I went to my GP with a breast lump ... [he] sent a referral letter stating 'over-anxious patient, had nervous breakdown at age 17' (20 years ago!). Consequently I was greeted by the specialist with 'well, you're a bit of a worrier, aren't you? Every physical illness I have had for the last 20 years has first been dismissed as anxiety, depression or stress." [134]

12. People with mental health problems frequently report stigma and discrimination in health services.[135] Research found that 44 per cent reported discrimination from GPs, such as physical health complaints not being taken seriously.[136] 18 per cent would not disclose their mental health problems to a GP for fear of discrimination.

Taking part in the community

"I feel alone on the estate – they know about me and they shut me out." [137]

"I regularly get called 'pervert' when I go out of my house, by the five year old kids in the street. Sometimes I stay at home because I can't run the gauntlet for that day. Hence, although there may be lots of inclusive activities available, I am emotionally unable to access them."

13. 52 per cent of Social Exclusion Unit consultation respondents highlighted negative attitudes in the community towards people with mental health problems, ranging from avoidance to prejudice and outright hostility. This is consistent with other research findings.[138]

Public education programme, London

A study of local attitudes around a new community-based group home for people with mental health problems in South London found that local residents were willing to help, but lacked information. After a public education programme, local residents were over three times more likely to have visited the home than those in a control area. 13 per cent, compared with none in the control area, had invited people into their homes. The majority of people in the home (compared with none in the control area) said they had some contact with local residents. The research was funded by the Department of Health and North East Thames Regional Health Authority.

14. Mental health problems can affect and lead to the breakdown of family relationships. For example, one study found that a woman was not invited to family events such as Sunday lunch, while the personal appearance of another was criticised in terms relating to her mental health.[139]

15. Stigma and fear in ethnic minority communities, in combination with a distrust of mental health services, means that ethnic minorities often seek professional help at a very late stage and come to the attention of services with more serious levels of distress.[140] Once in services, they can face discrimination based on racial prejudice. Misunderstandings about religious and spiritual beliefs can also lead to discrimination. Other people with mental health problems who may face such double discrimination include those with physical or sensory impairments, and gay, lesbian or bisexual people.

16. It can be almost impossible to guarantee confidentiality in very close-knit rural communities if an individual needs to use mental health services. This can lead to greater stigma and isolation if the individual is not accepted as part of the community, although the reverse can also be true: if the individual is well known, the community might be better able to 'see the person and not the problem'.

Police

17. Anecdotal evidence from Social Exclusion Unit visits and the consultation suggested that police officers can lack understanding of mental health problems and not know how best to help in a crisis situation. Police officers are often the first to be called to any incident of a person experiencing a mental health crisis,[141] yet research into the views of the Metropolitan police force found that police officers often had very negative attitudes towards mental health issues.[142] Other than basic foundation training, police officers currently receive no standard training in mental health awareness and recognition, yet spend a significant amount of their time interacting with people with mental health problems – one survey estimated this at up to 200 contacts per day across six forces.[143]

Mental health awareness training, Northumbria police

The Northumbria police force is piloting a training course totalling 40 hours on mental health awareness for operational officers within specialist units. The course includes mental health services, communication techniques, recognition of symptoms and behaviour, medication, and methods of defusing conflict. It was developed after a survey and an earlier pilot course aimed at patrol officers suggested that officers would welcome additional training on mental health issues, with the great majority believing that mental health should be a higher priority within the police service. The training was developed and delivered in partnership between people with mental health problems, police officers and mental health service providers. Independent evaluation by the University of Newcastle suggested it resulted in quicker incident responses, shorter incidents, more appropriate resolutions, reduced potential for violent confrontations and improved attitudes towards mental health issues among officers. The evaluation also highlighted the very positive view of such an initiative amongst the mental health community.

Education

18. Many surveys have found that children and young people are less tolerant of people with mental health problems than adults.[144,145] Around one quarter of parents with mental health problems said their children had been teased or bullied, or they were afraid that it might happen.
"My children were teased both at school and on the streets near home about my condition. I was referred to as a 'psycho'."[146]

19. Most children learn about emotional health and well-being in schools as part of **Personal, Social and Health Education**, within the context of learning about developing a healthy lifestyle and discrimination. There is no requirement for schools to include learning about mental health. The **National Healthy School Standard**, jointly funded by the Department of Health and Department for Education and Skills, aims to improve standards of health and education in schools, promote social inclusion and tackle health inequalities. Mental health stigma and discrimination are not addressed. Education in **Social, Emotional and Behavioural Skills** aims to help children develop self-awareness, motivation and empathy, and deal with feelings and social situations. It is being trialled in selected primary schools.

School workshops, Maidstone and Sevenoaks

In 2001, Maidstone and Sevenoaks mental health awareness groups, with the Institute of Psychiatry and Rethink, delivered short workshops within the Personal, Social, and Health Education curriculum for students aged 14-15 to increase mental health awareness and challenge negative stereotypes associated with severe mental health problems. The workshops were supported by leaflets specifically designed for young people. They were facilitated by people with experience of mental health problems and those who worked in the mental health field. They had a significant impact on attitudes, even after six months. Changes were most marked for female students and those reporting personal contact with people with mental health problems.[147]

What is being done to tackle stigma?

20. The **National Service Framework for Mental Health** (Standard One) aims to ensure that health and social services promote mental health and reduce discrimination and social exclusion, although in practice funding can be limited at local level. The National Institute for Mental Health in England (NIMHE) has lead responsibility for tackling stigma and discrimination around mental health problems.

21. There has been considerable effort to tackle stigma in England, but this has not always been well co-ordinated, and has focused on education and awareness rather than achieving behavioural change. The Royal College of Psychiatrists' five-year 'Changing Minds' campaign ended in late 2003. The Department of Health ran a three-year campaign, *mindout for mental health*, that ended in March 2004. A number of voluntary organisations also have ongoing campaigning work.

Open Up

Mental Health Media has launched Open Up, a project that provides a 'toolkit' of training, support and resources to enable people with experience of mental health problems to take positive action against discrimination in local communities. Open Up has set up five development areas across England and Wales, and offers free anti-discrimination courses and local co-ordinators in those areas. A website with resources and networking tools **www.openuptoolkit.net** provides online support, and a complete set of multimedia resources will be launched in July 2004. Open Up was launched in 2002 with £500,000 in grants.

22. Two key lessons from the *mindout* campaign were the need for longer-term funding strategies and robust evaluation. A literature review of international work to tackle stigma, discrimination and prejudice around mental health commissioned by NIMHE found that average spending on mental health awareness in England is lower and more short-term than in countries with more successful programmes.[148]

International spend on mental health campaigns per head of the general population[149]

Mindout for mental health	1.44 pence
See Me, Scotland	13 pence[150]
Like Minds, Like Mine, New Zealand	$NZ1 (approx 36 pence)

(Figures are an approximation of overall spend divided by population, with annual spend averaged over the campaign.)

***See Me* campaign, Scotland**

See Me is an anti-stigma campaign run by an alliance of five Scottish mental health organisations and supported by the Scottish Executive. The campaign is a major part of the National Programme for Improving Mental Health and Well-being. It was launched in October 2002, and has almost £3 million of funding over four years (to 2005-06)[151]. It has been developed through extensive consultation with people with experience of mental health issues. The campaign works on a national level, underpinned by local activities. It uses multimedia advertising, supported by people with mental health problems trained to speak to the media. See Me includes a 'stigma stopwatch' that encourages people to respond to discriminating attitudes and language in the media. Recognition of the campaign has been maintained at 28 per cent.

23. Face-to-face contact and community engagement are often the most effective ways to reduce stigma and discrimination.[152] *Mindout* had an Ambassador Bureau with more than 40 people with experience of mental health problems who were trained to speak to the media and employers about their experiences. Evaluation found that ambassadors were perceived to make the campaign 'human and personal', and that hearing first-hand about mental health problems challenged misconceptions. NIMHE plans to build on the ambassadors model in its future work.

24. Ofcom, the independent regulator for the UK communications industries, has established an advisory committee on older and disabled people, whose remit will include issues of portrayal of disabled people in broadcast media. Ofcom will inform the committee of emerging trends arising from complaints and through ongoing viewer research. Although its advisory committee has yet to set out its priorities for its first year, early signs are that they may wish to investigate the impact of stereotyping and negative portrayal of people with mental health problems to advise Ofcom whether further research should be commissioned.

25. Recent literature on tackling discrimination and stigma suggests the need for a rights-based approach, aiming to change attitudes through awareness education and behaviour through legislation, and has found that the most effective campaigns have sustained funding.[153]

Discrimination legislation

26. The **Disability Discrimination Act 1995** (DDA) was a milestone in reducing discrimination against people with disabilities. It outlaws discrimination against disabled people in employment, in relation to the supply of goods, facilities and services, in the disposal of premises, in education, and contains measures designed to facilitate access to certain types of public transport. It includes a duty on employers and service providers to make 'reasonable adjustments' to enable disabled people to work and access services.

27. The Disability Rights Commission (DRC) was established in 2000 to work towards the elimination of discrimination against disabled people, promote equality of opportunity for and good practice in the treatment of disabled people, and to keep the working of the DDA and DRC Act under review. Its role includes advising the government on the operation of the legislation, and it has powers to investigate and take enforcement action and provide assistance in relation to proceedings. The DRC's helpline advises disabled people about their rights, and employers, service providers, and educationalists about their responsibilities. The Commission prepares and issues statutory codes of practice that give practical guidance on DDA legislation, publishes leaflets targeted at particular sectors, and runs an information website.

28. To claim protection under the DDA, a person must have a physical or mental impairment that has a substantial and long-term adverse effect on their ability to carry out normal day-to-day activities. Impairments arising from mental illness have to be clinically well-recognised. 'Long-term' means that it has lasted or is expected to last for 12 months or more. The number of disabled people with mental health problems in Britain covered by the DDA definition is estimated to be 580,783, just over 10 per cent of the total DDA disabled population of working age.[154]

Changes to the DDA

From October 2004, employment regulations will:

- extend to businesses with fewer than 15 employees;
- apply to police, prison officers and firefighters;
- define harassment related to disability and clarify that harassment is unlawful;
- ensure that treatment constituting direct discrimination against a disabled person – for example, where motivated by prejudice – can never be justified; and
- outlaw discriminatory job advertisements.

29. In December 2003, the government published a draft Disability Discrimination Bill that includes a duty for public bodies to promote equality of opportunity for disabled people, similar to that in the Race Relations (Amendment) Act 2000; and an extension of Part 3 of the DDA, covering service provision, to the statutory functions of public bodies.

30. The DRC has recommended changes to the legislation relating to mental health including:

- removing the need for mental illness to be 'clinically well-recognised';
- amending the list of daily activities covered by the DDA to reflect the way in which someone's ability to communicate may be affected by mental health problems; and
- amending the requirement that mental impairments should last for 12 months, to cover short-term depression.

In May 2004, the report of the Joint Scrutiny Committee on the Draft Disability Discrimination Bill included similar recommendations.

31. The government responded to the DRC in December 2003 that this is an area for possible future consideration and it is expected to respond to the recommendations of the Joint Scrutiny Committee in the near future.

32. People with mental health problems may not necessarily view themselves as 'disabled', and may not be aware of their rights under the DDA. Similarly, awareness amongst employers about how the DDA applies for people with mental health problems does not appear particularly strong.

33. Each year, between 10 and 15 per cent of all calls to the DRC helpline relate to people with mental health problems. 23 per cent of employment cases brought by the DRC are related to mental health.[155] Analysis found that employment tribunal applicants with 'depression, bad nerves and anxiety' had a success rate of 18 per cent, compared with 39 per cent for diabetes, the most successful applicant group.[156]

34. Recent government amendments to the Criminal Justice Act 2003 introduced tougher sentences for offences aggravated by hostility towards the victim because of his or her sexuality or disability, including mental health.

35. In October 2003, the government announced plans to set up the Commission for Equality and Human Rights, a single equality commission that would replace the Commission for Racial Equality, the Equal Opportunities Commission and the DRC. It would also take responsibility for new areas of discrimination law outlawing workplace discrimination on age, religion or belief and sexual orientation. In May 2004, the Department for Trade and Industry issued a White Paper, *Fairness for All: A New Commission for Equality and Human Rights*, ahead of a formal consultation in the summer.

Conclusion

Stigma and discrimination can have a greater impact on people's lives than the mental health problems themselves. Despite the variety of national and local campaigns, stigma and discrimination remain widespread. However, international evidence suggests that campaign work can be effective if properly funded and targeted.

The government will develop a strengthened programme to tackle stigma and discrimination. This will be led by the National Institute for Mental Health in England, working closely with other government departments, people with experience of mental health problems and the voluntary sector. NIMHE will also work with the Department for Education and Skills to develop resources for schools.

The Disability Discrimination Act marked a milestone in reducing disability-related discrimination, but some people with mental health problems may not view themselves as 'disabled', and remain unaware of the protection it offers. NIMHE will work with the Disability Rights Commission to raise awareness of the rights of people with mental health problems under the DDA.

CHAPTER 4: The role of health and social care services in preventing social exclusion

Summary

- Health and social care services play a critical role in enabling people to work and maintain social contacts, both of which are strongly associated with better mental health outcomes and reduced reliance on services.
- While there is already much good practice, low expectations and negative assumptions among health and social care staff about the abilities of people with mental health problems can inhibit progress. The new mental health workforce provides an important opportunity to change attitudes and place greater focus on employment and social inclusion issues.
- GPs do not always have the time or training to address vocational and social issues in depth. Advisers based in primary care have been introduced in some areas with encouraging results.
- Inequalities in access to health services can prevent vulnerable groups from receiving appropriate treatment and support. The physical health needs of people with mental health problems should not be overlooked.

Health and social care services

> *"As a hospital manager ... I see first hand how quick we are to remove people from society and how reluctant we often are to return them because we worry about the harm they may do to themselves. Yet we do not view the isolation, exclusion and removal of rights as harmful."*

1. Adults with mental health problems can spend significant amounts of time in contact with health and social care services. Doctors and other professionals can have a major impact on confidence and aspirations, and support people to retain jobs and social contacts. However, too many professionals believe that people with mental health problems should not work, even though for many, waiting to get well enough to work is not helpful, as inactivity is strongly associated with worsening mental health. The links between mental health and employment are discussed further in Chapter 5.

Current government policy

The **National Service Framework (NSF) for Mental Health** (1999) set out a major programme of reform, modernisation and investment for mental health services. It recognises the importance of tackling stigma and promoting social inclusion. The **National Institute for Mental Health in England (NIMHE)** provides support for implementation.

In addition, the NHS Plan (2000) has led to the introduction of new mental health workers:

- 1,000 new **graduate mental health workers** to treat and manage common mental health disorders in primary care;
- 500 new **gateway workers** to link between primary care and specialist services; and
- 'Support, Time and Recovery' or **STR workers**, located in health, social care, housing or employment schemes.

Under the **Shifting the Balance of Power** initiative, primary care trusts now receive 75 per cent of the total NHS budget and commission mental health services to meet the needs of their local populations.

The Department of Health has announced its intention to develop a vision and framework for adult social care, which will include mental health.

Primary care

"My GP told me that I would never work again."

2. Approximately nine out of ten adults with mental health problems, and one quarter with severe mental health problems receive all their support from primary care.[157] Around 30 per cent of GP consultations concern mental health problems, usually depression, eating disorders and anxiety disorders.[158] GP interest in mental health varies: one survey found that 34 per cent of GPs want to spend more time on mental health and 24 per cent want to spend less.[159]

3. GPs issue sickness certificates when they assess that a person cannot perform their usual work. Mental health problems are more likely to be listed on sickness certificates in the most deprived areas of the country.

Figure 8: Sick note diagnosis and social deprivation

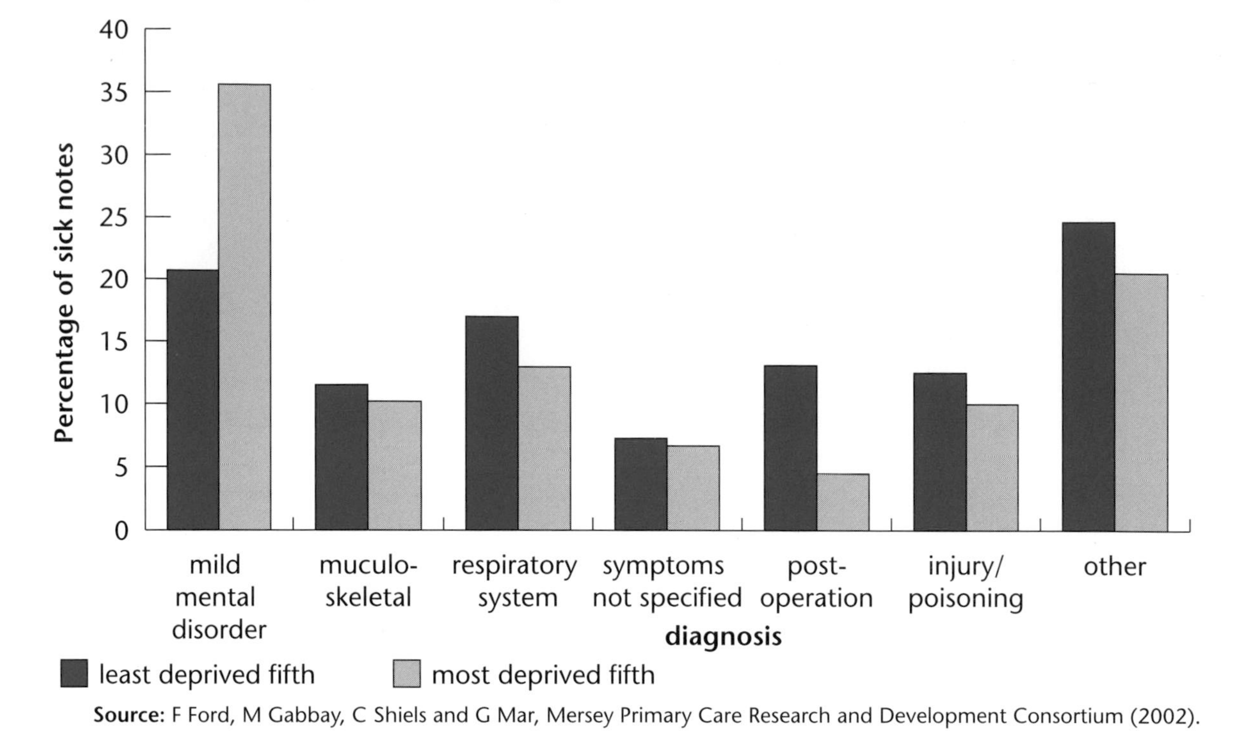

Source: F Ford, M Gabbay, C Shiels and G Mar, Mersey Primary Care Research and Development Consortium (2002).

4. Nearly one-fifth of respondents to the Social Exclusion Unit consultation argued that mental health services needed to become more **socially focused** and less medical in their approach. This includes offering more social activities rather than medical solutions to mental health problems. In a recent survey, more than 80 per cent of GPs openly admitted over-prescribing anti-depressants such as *Prozac* and *Seroxat* to patients suffering from depression, anxiety or stress.[160]

5. The graph below shows the rapid increase in drugs prescriptions and drug costs over the past ten years.[161]

Figure 9: Net ingredient cost of prescription items dispensed in the community for treatment of mental health problems

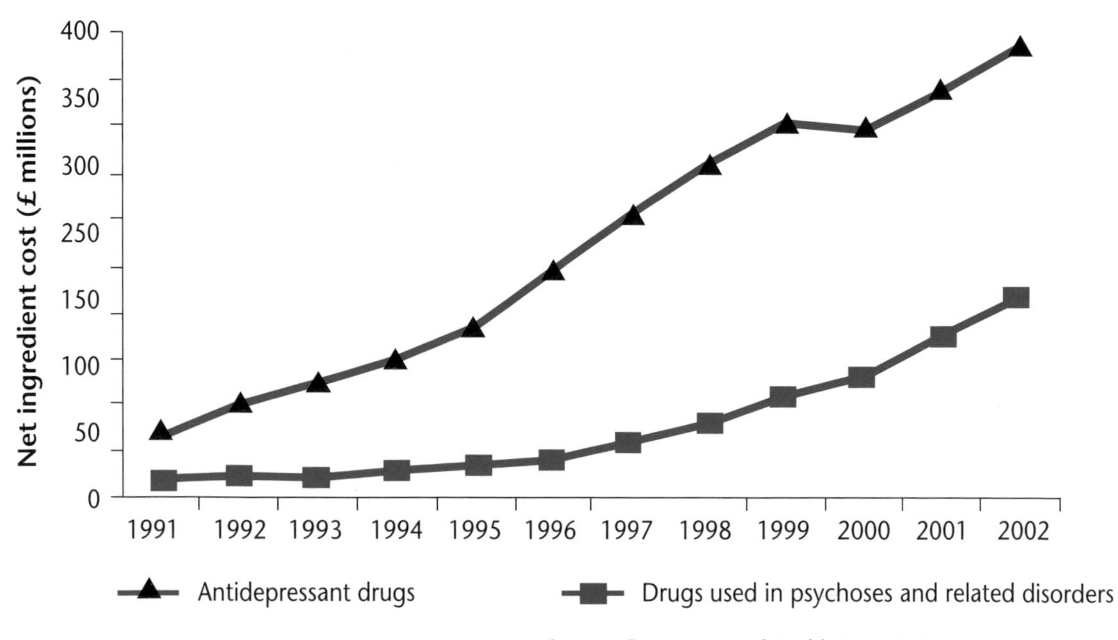

Source: Department of Health Prescription Cost Analysis System.

6. The General Medical Services (GMS) contract, introduced in 2003, rewards practices for high quality evidence-based care, and offers flexibility to provide additional services. Primary Care Trusts (PCTs) can commission an enhanced level of care from some practices for the provision of services, including depression, drug or alcohol misuse and services for homeless people. There is increased flexibility to commission services from new providers, for example, working with the voluntary sector on new mental health helplines aimed at particular sections of the community such as Muslim women or Chinese people.[162] The GMS contract has two elements of funding: a basic payment for every practice, and further payments for quality and outcomes. Only 4 per cent of possible further payments relate to mental health.

Advice and support in primary care

> *"I would like to expand the current services which are only accessible after a psychiatric diagnosis to take a more preventative approach by picking people up in primary care before major problems develop."*
>
> *"The surgery was definitely the most convenient place, I wouldn't have gone anywhere else."* [163]

7. Advice within primary care can be particularly important, as adults may not be in touch with other services. There are different ways that this can be provided. Shared characteristics of effective advice services include a non-stigmatising, accessible location, with ease of referral, and the adviser acting as a gateway to opportunities in the wider community.

8. **Vocational and benefits advisers** can help reduce demands on GPs' time and are highly valued by customers. In Lewisham, there are three full-time advisers, funded by the PCT, covering 13 different surgeries.

Health Plus, Bradford

Health Plus is a PCT-funded project with advisers in 30 GP surgeries focusing on benefits, debt, housing, employment and immigration rights. Staff are provided by local advice agencies. 30 per cent of referrals come from GPs and 30 per cent from outside the health practice, including family, friends and self-referrals. Almost three-quarters seek benefits advice. Evaluation found Health Plus saved time for GPs and nursing staff, and reduced stress/anxiety levels and improved the quality of life for clients.

9. A number of projects support 'social prescribing' by GPs. These projects can increase social networks and opportunities.

- The National Institute for Adult Continuing Education supports over 20 **prescriptions for learning** projects in England. In the Nottingham pilot, 65 per cent of clients referred had no qualifications, and almost all said that they would not have taken up learning without the help of the project. One-quarter reported improvements in their mental health.[164]

- **Exercise on prescription** projects allow GPs to refer people to leisure centres or gyms. Studies have shown that patients respond well to GP advice to take more exercise[165] and such schemes are beneficial to health, with reduced prescription medicines and improved quality of living.[166]

- **Arts on prescription** projects arrange referrals to local arts organisations. Early evaluation showed a reduction in the number of recognisable mental health problems.[167]

10. One Plus One has developed *Brief Encounters* training for health visitors to improve a primary care team's ability to respond, identify and help with relationship problems between parents which can be increased or provoked following a birth. These problems are often associated with post-natal depression and can have a significant impact on family wellbeing. Research has shown that when the health visitors were trained, parents were 75 per cent more likely to have received help. No mothers used counselling – they all preferred the health visitors.[168]

11. Some people, particularly those with complex needs, may benefit from support from an **advocate** to maximise their decision-making capacity and participation, to help them think what they want to say and express their views. The role of advocates in helping with housing issues is discussed in Chapter 8.

Access to talking therapies

12. Availability of talking therapies varies as a result of staff shortages and local decisions on how to meet population needs. This can lead to long waiting lists, poor co-ordination between services and a lack of partnership working. 11 per cent of respondents to the Social Exclusion Unit consultation identified the need for more access to psychological interventions, such as **counselling**.

13. Take-up of, and access to talking therapies varies. Only 25 per cent of those accessing the student counselling service are male, even though young men are a particularly high suicide risk group.[169] Adults from ethnic minorities are less likely to be referred for psychotherapy, psychological treatments, counselling or other complementary treatments.[170] Many people appear to pay privately for talking therapies due to the lack of availability within the NHS. Lower socio-economic groups can therefore have limited access if they are unable to pay for treatment.

14. Systematic information about waiting times for psychological therapy is not currently collected centrally. The Healthcare Commission will work with the Department of Health to consider whether and how to develop an indicator for inclusion in future Trust performance indicators.

15. **National Institute for Clinical Excellence (NICE)** guidelines indicated that all people with schizophrenia should have access to cognitive behavioural therapy or family therapy. NICE guidelines on **depression** and **anxiety** are expected in 2004, recommending a range of talking therapies for mild to moderate depression and specific talking treatments for moderate to severe. However, although the number of practice counsellors has grown rapidly, they may not be able to provide the level of therapies suggested. A report has been published from the psychotherapy sub-group of the Mental Health Care Group Workforce Team on the steps needed to deliver cost-effective, safe, user-friendly, comprehensive and accessible talking therapies.[171]

Physical health problems

16. People with mental health problems have a higher risk of premature death.[172] A person with schizophrenia can expect to live for **ten years less** than someone without a mental health problem, mainly because of **physical health problems**.[173] Poor physical health can also lead to mental health problems. An estimated 70 per cent of all new cases of depression in older people are caused by poor physical health.[174]

17. People with severe mental health problems are likely to eat less well, smoke more heavily and take less exercise than the general population,[175] resulting in a **higher risk of cardiovascular disease**.[176] They are up to three times more likely to be dependent on **alcohol**,[177] and deaths from **smoking**-related diseases are twice as high among people with schizophrenia.[178] Adults with common mental health problems have been found to be twice as likely to smoke as those with no mental health problems.[179] Deaths from infectious diseases, endocrine, circulatory, respiratory, digestive and genito-urinary system disorders have all been reported as significantly more likely for adults with severe mental health problems.[180] Similarly, sustained stress or trauma may increase susceptibility to viral infection and physical illness by damaging the immune system.[181] People from ethnic minority groups are more likely to have poor physical health.

18. Adults with severe mental health problems should have regular reviews of medication, alcohol and drug use, smoking, heart disease and risk of diabetes. In reality, they are less likely to be offered such reviews than other members of the general population.[182]

19. *Tackling Health Inequalities: A programme for action* sets out plans to tackle health inequalities over the next three years and to achieve the national target for 2010 to reduce inequalities in health outcomes by 10 per cent.[183] Addressing inequalities in the physical health of adults with mental health problems will contribute to achieving this target. A White Paper on improving health is being developed, informed by the *Choosing Health?* consultation, which included mental health as one of its themes.

Secondary Care

> *"I'm scared of turning into the people I've seen in the day-centre. I know I have a mental health problem, but I'm not like that. I want a way forward, not just sitting there, just drinking tea and talking about the side effects of various medication."*

20. Secondary care services provided by mental health trusts have an important role to promote social and vocational opportunities for people with severe and enduring mental health problems. The advice and support people first receive can influence their success in retaining their current occupation, and impact on self-confidence and future aspirations.

21. Multi-disciplinary **Community Mental Health Teams (CMHTs)** are the central hub of adult mental health services. They support people with complex mental health problems and their families in the community when their needs cannot be met by GPs or generic social services. Patients are referred back to their GP when their condition has improved. CMHTs also provide long-term care of people with enduring mental health problems.

22. The transition between primary and secondary services can be problematic. Up to 28 per cent of referrals from primary care to specialist services are inappropriate.[184] Referrals to secondary services can also be stigmatising and there are people with severe mental health problems who choose not to access specialist services.

23. **Acute psychiatric inpatient services** are for people who cannot be treated and supported at home or in a less restrictive setting.[185] Staff should identify if people are in employment or education at the time of admission, maintain contact with families, and help resolve any financial issues. However, work pressures can lead to these issues being overlooked.

24. The **Care Programme Approach (CPA)** is the framework for assessment and care planning to address the needs of people using specialist mental health services.[186] Following an assessment of need, a care plan should be drawn up in consultation with the individual and, as appropriate, their carer. The care plan should be regularly reviewed and updated as necessary. A care co-ordinator should be appointed to keep in close contact with the individual and monitor and co-ordinate their care.

25. Standard five of the Mental Health NSF set a target that by March 2002, all written care plans for people on enhanced CPA must show plans to secure suitable employment or other occupational activity. A number of mental health trusts positively promote employment opportunities for people with mental health problems within their own organisations.

26. Effective care co-ordination should take a broad view and include housing, education, caring responsibilities, employment, benefits advice and leisure.[187] In practice, plans often tend to focus on health needs, with social and vocational needs taking a secondary place and not always clearly reflected. However, some services have developed their CPA process to ensure that these issues are regularly considered.

Care Programme Approach, Rotherham

As part of the Care Programme Approach (CPA) process for people with mental health problems, Rotherham Mental Health Services carry out an Occupational Needs Assessment and identify occupational goals. These are a core part of the CPA process and the actions are reviewed at CPA meetings.

Rotherham's Health and Social Care Community relaunched the CPA documentation in 2001. The Educational, Training and Employment (ETE) service made a fundamental change to the process of identifying and addressing occupational need within the full needs assessment. In conjunction with Rotherham Service User Monitoring Team, an occupational self-assessment was developed and enables an individual to highlight their personal strengths and skills. Identifying meaningful goals forms the initial stage of referral to the ETE Service. Feedback from people with mental health problems highlighted that meaningful activity and the support of multi-agency partnerships were valued and important.

27. Variations have been highlighted in the level to which services involve people in planning their own care.[188] Some people report not feeling actively involved in the process of agreeing plans and setting goals and have turned to other approaches as a way of taking more control of this for themselves.[189]

David's story – care planning

David works part-time as a service user consultant for his local mental health trust. He first experienced depression at the age of 18 and continues to see his consultant psychiatrist for help with this. Although his treatment is reviewed every six months, David reports that he has not seen a copy of his care plan nor had it discussed with him. In his experience, certain issues do not get sufficiently addressed within the Care Programme Approach planning process, particularly around physical health, work and education.

Last year, David attended a training course on 'planning for yourself'. He has used this approach in his own life to:

- identify where his support comes from, how people around him can contribute to him staying well and what they need to know to help him;
- set out his ambitions and goals for the future; and
- plan for times of crisis.

Although considering that people may need some help in developing their own plans and recommending that the paperwork is kept to a minimum, David thinks that 'essential lifestyle planning' could be used alongside or to expand the CPA process. In particular, he feels that this approach provides a framework for building on his strengths and achievements, focusing on the things that matter to him and planning his life on a daily basis in a way that contributes to realising his long-term aims.

28. The NHS Plan introduced specialist teams in secondary care, with significant potential to build in a stronger focus on vocational and social issues.

- **Early intervention teams** provide community-based treatment and support to young people aged 14-35 years with first episode psychosis. This should include ensuring that involvement in education and work is maintained, and future prospects are not unnecessarily jeopardised.

- **Assertive outreach teams** target adults aged 18-65 years with severe and enduring mental health problems, and additional complex needs such as homelessness, self-harm or neglect, or high levels of disability. Assertive outreach can achieve better outcomes than standard community care on accommodation status, employment and patient satisfaction.[190]

- **Crisis resolution teams** aim to prevent the need for hospitalisation for adults having an acute psychiatric crisis. They provide 24-hour community-based treatment until the crisis is resolved.

Antenna Outreach Service, Haringey, London

Since 1999, Antenna has worked with 200 Black African or African Caribbean people aged 16-25 who suffer mental distress. It is funded by the Primary Care and Mental Health Trust. At referral, 60 per cent have lost contact with friends, and 45 per cent had been involved in a violent incident. The service has links with a range of young people's services in North London, and will support mainstream providers working with young people with mental health problems. It has also developed a home tuition scheme, sports and graphic design courses, a music group and opportunities for people with mental health problems to volunteer for community work through local churches. All these build contact between people with mental health problems and the rest of the community, and aim to develop skills that facilitate a move out of the mental health sector into mainstream activities.

29. A draft **Mental Health Bill** is expected to be published this year for pre-legislative scrutiny. It will make provisions for the compulsory care and treatment of people with mental health problems who are considered to be a danger either to themselves or others. People subject to compulsory care and treatment are likely to need significant support to prevent their social exclusion and enable them to continue to participate in community life.

Day services

30. In 2002-03, health and social care spent £140 million on **day and employment services** for adults with severe mental health problems in England[191] (employment projects are discussed further in Chapter 5). Traditionally, day services have often focused on specialist support services that are solely for people with mental health problems. They often provide a 'one-stop shop', providing a practical place of support during the day, as well as access to other services and advice.

Day services, Redcar and Cleveland Mind

Redcar and Cleveland Mind day services provide a safe and supportive environment seven days a week for adults with mental health problems, as well as acting as an information resource for the general public. The service has strong links with local providers, including the Citizens Advice Bureau and local colleges. They provide opportunities for people using the service to participate in the planning and delivery of mental health services. The service has helped people progress from being volunteers to paid employment. Some people have done a walking leaders course at a local college so that they can lead walks with their peers in the day service.

31. As a general rule, day services are valued by staff and people with mental health problems, as they provide a place to go, opportunities to meet other people, and something to do during the day. However, there is wide variation in the standards of day services. Traditional day services have often not focused on social inclusion, offering little or no contact with people outside mental health services, and limited opportunities for people to develop the skills to progress to using mainstream provision. The stereotypical image of a day centre where people sit around all day, smoking and drinking tea, still exists in some places. However, in recent years there has been a move towards increasing integration with mainstream services and the wider community.

Modernising day services, Gateshead Council

Gateshead Council, in partnership with South of the Tyne and Wearside Mental Health Trust and the voluntary sector, is currently modernising its day services for people with mental health problems. The focus of the modernisation programme is to facilitate recovery and social inclusion and enable people with mental health problems and their carers to engage in meaningful, integrated, community activities and lead ordinary lives. Support will be provided for opportunities related to employment and meaningful occupation, education and social and leisure activities, based upon individual aspiration and taking account of different religious, spiritual and cultural needs. The Council will continue to provide a traditional day service on a limited basis for current users who will also be offered the opportunity to engage in more mainstream integrated opportunities. The modernisation and reprovision programme will also allow for the further development of a Crisis Response and Acute Day Treatment service and for investment in user-led and carers services, in accordance with emerging priorities.

32. Modernised day services have an important role in supporting people to access mainstream community services outside the mental health sector. This might be through offering taster courses, or having a worker accompany the individual to mainstream services. Day services can also offer advocacy for people with mental health problems, to allow them to take decisions and participate more fully in community activities. Where services have been redesigned, there has often been initial opposition to the change, but outcomes and the range of services for people with mental health problems have improved over time.

Imagine, Mainstream project, Liverpool

Imagine is a voluntary sector organisation that runs the Mainstream project. Mainstream supports people with mental health problems to access mainstream provision rather than just mental health services. Each staff member ('Bridge Builder') is responsible for making links with a particular sector and supporting clients in these areas. Sectors include education and training; employment; visual and performing arts; sports and leisure; volunteering; and faith, spirituality and cultural communities. Clients define their own support needs and aspirations, and the client and bridge builder identify possible opportunities to meet these in mainstream settings. Bridge builders offer dedicated, tailored support to clients as they develop the confidence to use mainstream services and further develop social networks.

Direct payments

33. Under legislation passed in 1996, disabled people have the legal right to receive payment of community care monies and are able directly to purchase their own care, based on an agreed needs-led assessment.[192] More recently, eligibility for direct payments has also been extended to carers.[193] Direct payments offer people with mental health problems and carers greater flexibility around their support arrangements and the means by which their needs can be met, in particular to facilitate access to mainstream services.[194] Direct payments aim to promote independence and inclusion in local communities by offering opportunities for rehabilitation, education, leisure and employment.

34. Local authorities now have to make direct payments to those who are eligible and want them. However, take-up by people with mental health problems has been very poor,[195] with the lowest rate of take up compared to other eligible adult groups.[196] Figures from 2003 show that only 229 people with mental health problems had taken this route. Few people from ethnic minority groups with mental health problems are accessing direct payments despite their potential for facilitating individual and culturally sensitive support.[197] Studies have shown that inadequate leadership, a lack of awareness about and promotion of direct payments, and staff concerns about people's ability to manage payments have hindered greater take-up.[198]

Cultural change in health and social care

"Most of us have been told that we'll never get better, or if we do that we will relapse."

35. In meetings with the Social Exclusion Unit, people with mental health problems and those working in the mental health field have often raised concerns that health and social care staff's **low expectations**, negative attitudes, and assumptions about the abilities of people with mental health problems inhibited progress.

Training

36. A survey in 1999 found that only one-third of GPs had had mental health training in the previous five years, while one in ten expressed concerns about their training or skills needs in mental health.[199] Roughly half of trainee GPs spend six months working in psychiatry as part of their training. Only 2 per cent of practice nurses have received formal mental health training.[200] The three-year NIMHE National Primary Care Mental Health Programme was launched in 2003 to improve the standard and consistency of service offered.

37. Current professional training for other health and social care professionals who have specialist mental health training, such as occupational therapists, nurses, psychologists, psychiatrists and social workers, include aspects of social inclusion. However, they do not always focus on the importance of or mechanisms for achieving appropriate social outcomes. Work is needed to ensure that pre- and post-qualification training is influenced by the new national occupational standards for mental health, and that the shared capabilities framework for all mental health workers is implemented. Individual professions are already making such changes. For example, the College of Occupational Therapists is developing a strategy for occupational therapy staff in mental health to progress individualised inclusive practice that reflects social inclusion objectives.

Involving adults with mental health problems in the design and delivery of services

38. Nearly one-third of respondents to the Social Exclusion Unit consultation felt that increased involvement of adults with mental health problems in the design and delivery of mental health services would help promote social inclusion. For many service users and carers, the NHS Plan (2000) offered the first opportunity to play a key role in the design, delivery, planning, monitoring and evaluation of health services. A **Patient and Public Involvement Forum** has been set up for every NHS trust and primary care Trust in England, to allow local people to play an active role in decision making. Mental Health **Local Implementation Teams** are expected to have representation from people with mental health problems, carers and the voluntary sector.

39. The **Expert Patients Programme**, set up in April 2002, is an NHS-based training programme to help people living with long-term chronic conditions to develop new skills to manage their condition better. Expert patients will include people with long-standing mental health problems such as bipolar disorder.

40. People's involvement can be affected by uncertainty about how to pay them for their contribution. Various attempts have been made to offer guidance on payments[201] and participation[202], but a survey of organisations commissioning and providing secondary mental health services revealed that:

- half had unwritten policies based on past practice and only a small number had robust policies for participation payments. Only one-sixth claimed their policy was effective;
- levels of payment varied significantly. About two-thirds paid only basic expenses, and only a quarter to a third of organisations funded practical support (such as transport, advocates/supporters, childcare); and
- concerns were expressed that people with mental health problems could have state benefits reduced if they were paid for their work.[203] The rules surrounding benefits and paid work are discussed further in Chapter 6.

Pathways to health and social care services for different groups

41. Access to health and social care services varies, resulting in some groups presenting later to mental health services when their mental health problems may be worse.

> *"An African-Caribbean man with a diagnosis of schizophrenia may be particularly reluctant to disclose, given powerful 'big, black and dangerous' stereotypes."* [204]

42. **Ethnicity:** in February 2004, the formal enquiry into the death of David Bennett concluded that discrimination existed throughout the NHS and that *"people from black and minority ethnic communities find it difficult to access mental health services."*[205] Adults from ethnic minority groups have higher levels of dissatisfaction with statutory services than white people, and are twice as likely to disagree with their diagnosis.[206] Black and South Asian patients are less likely to have their mental health problems detected by a GP, but more likely to have their problems wrongly attributed to mental ill health.[207]

43. There is limited data on the ethnicity of people using mental health services. People from ethnic minority groups are over-represented in secure institutions and prisons: one study found that black people were twice as likely to be involuntarily detained under the Mental Health Act than white people.[208] Ethnic minorities are more likely to enter mental health services after initial contact with the police, other forensic services or referrals from strangers rather than a relative or a neighbour, although are no more likely to be aggressive before admission.[209] At the end of 2004, a baseline census will be conducted on the ethnicity of people using mental health services.

Delivering Race Equality: A Framework for Action

In October 2003, the Department of Health launched *Delivering Race Equality: A Framework for Action* for consultation. This sets out what those who plan, deliver and monitor local primary care and mental health services should do for people with mental health problems and carers from ethnic minority groups. It asked for views on the national action needed to provide support and leadership. The framework is built around improved information, more appropriate and responsive services, and better community engagement. It seeks to improve suicide rates, acute inpatient facilities and aversive pathways to care.

44. NIMHE is working with the University of Central Lancashire to implement a model of **community engagement**, to encourage greater involvement in the design, development and delivery of local services. The model will raise awareness of mental health problems, reduce discrimination, increase employment and help to bridge the gap between mainstream services and ethnic minority communities. NIMHE is currently considering whether this model of community engagement can be more widely adopted to reach other groups who may not always be well served by the traditional approach of mental health services.

Cares of Life, Southwark, London

The Cares of Life project in Southwark, London (South London & Maudsley NHS Trust) is an innovative community based model of care which aims to improve mental health services for African and Caribbean people who are experiencing common mental health problems. The service is provided by graduate community health workers who are members of the local communities, and who have been trained to use psychological interventions and to work closely with informal support networks provided by barbers, hairdressers, churches, faith groups and youth clubs. People with mental health problems are referred by lay health volunteers who have been recruited from the informal support networks and who have been trained to recognise symptoms of mental health problems.

45. **Age:** Child and Adolescent Mental Health Services (CAMHS) are a key source of support, advice and intervention for children and young people with mental health problems. However, only around one in four 5-15 year olds with mental health problems is in contact with CAMHS, and around one in six have to wait more than six months for an appointment.[210] Research in 2001 found that half of young people's advice agencies could get virtually no help for 16-18s from CAMHS or adult services.[211] The government is investing an additional £300 million over the next three years to ensure that comprehensive services are available in all areas by 2006. The *Children's National Service Framework (NSF)*, which is due to be published later this year, will set out the standards and milestones for improvement in CAMHS services, including year-on-year improvements in access. It is expected that over the period of implementation of the *NSF*, CAMHS will make the transition to covering the age range 0-18 years.[212]

Connexions, Humber

In 2001, a pilot project was launched to provide seamless support to young people across children's and adult's mental health services, and ensure that referrals to services are more appropriate. The project aims to enhance the skills of primary care teams to ensure that young people with less severe mental health problems can receive support through primary care, schools and Connexions rather than being unnecessarily referred to specialist services. At the same time, it aims to facilitate and speed up the referral to specialist services for those with serious mental health problems.

The project has created strong links between Connexions Humber and local partner organisations, including the University of Hull, Hull and East Riding Community NHS Trust, and Hull and East Yorkshire Mind. The project is currently being extended into more schools in Hull, with a view to extending across Hull and East Riding in the future.

46. People transferring from generic adult services to older people's services often face discontinuities of care just at the point at which their health needs are becoming more complex.[213] Depression and other mental health problems can be overlooked among older people, particularly those who live alone or in residential care, as they are seen as an inevitable consequence of ageing.

47. **Gender:** women-only and women-centred services are being developed to address concerns of harassment and abuse, take account of caring and other roles, and improve access to female staff. In 2002, the Department of Health published *Women's Mental Health: Into The Mainstream* to promote the strategic development of mental health care for women.

48. Departments across government have signed up to a wide range of commitments which are contained in the DTI's report *Delivering on Gender Equality* (June 2003). These aim to ensure that gender equality is achieved in all areas of government policy and practice. Women's life experiences and priorities are often different to men's and require a distinct response. This may include placing particular emphasis on finding suitable accommodation and securing custody of their children.

49. **Family status:** services do not always consider the parenting and caring responsibilities of people with mental health problems. Parents with severe and enduring mental health problems are rarely offered parenting and family support, and inpatient or day services may not be welcoming to children.[214] This is discussed in more detail in Chapter 7.

50. **Sexuality:** Many lesbian, gay and bisexual adults with mental health problems feel unable to seek help through traditional services but very few specialist services exist to meet their particular needs.

PACE, London

PACE was established in 1985 in response to a need within the lesbian and gay communities for a counselling and support agency that was genuinely responsive to their concerns. PACE is now London's largest provider of mental health and well-being services to the lesbian, gay and bisexual communities. Its range of services includes counselling, groupwork, mental health advocacy, employment, youthwork and family therapy services. All PACE services can be accessed by self-referral.

51. **Location:** Transport difficulties can make accessing services difficult, especially for those using public transport. This can be a particular problem in rural areas, where services might be further away. There can be high unit costs attached to delivering specialist services in rural areas, which can lead to specialist services only being available in towns. In 2002, 87 per cent of households were within four kilometres of a GP's surgery but these figures mask localised patterns of isolation.[215]

Rural Emotional Support Team (REST), Staffordshire

REST has four team members who have an agricultural background and have had mental health training. It operates in south and mid-Staffordshire, offering free and confidential services for people in agriculture and related jobs in a community covering 1000 square miles. It has an open referral policy and an active caseload of around 25 people, in line with the ratio of assertive outreach approaches. REST works to a budget of £100,000 per year. From June 2004 the organisation is applying for independent charity status and seeking ongoing funding.

52. People with **personality disorder** often find it difficult to obtain a diagnosis, have their condition understood, and support needs met. Diagnosis is often hidden from patients or wrongly identified.[216] Health and social care professionals often feel that they do not have the skills, training or resources to provide an adequate service.[217] NIMHE's *Personality disorder: No longer a diagnosis of exclusion* states that all trusts delivering mental health services need to consider the needs of people with a personality disorder.[218]

53. Mental health problems are often experienced by **adult victims of domestic violence** and those who have been **sexually abused in childhood**.[219] The effects are often not recognised or treated effectively by health and mental health services[220]. Joint initiatives between the Department of Health, NIMHE, the Home Office and other government departments are underway to develop services and support for victims of violence and abuse. These include: the appointment of a national domestic violence co-ordinator; work to map voluntary sector services and develop national service guidelines for treating the lifetime effects of child sexual abuse; and local work with police, health services and voluntary sector agencies.

54. Some people with mental health problems have **complex needs** and will require support across a range of other issues. This can make it more difficult to access mainstream mental health services or other aspects of social care.[221] A recent Institute for Public Policy Research/Turning Point report proposed 'connected care' centres as a single point of contact in deprived communities to fill the gap between housing, employment, health, social care and area-based regeneration initiatives.[222]

55. People with **drug or alcohol problems** can fall between services, particularly when neither the mental health problem nor substance misuse alone is severe enough to access specialist services. The causal relationship between mental health and substance misuse problems is complex, making primary diagnosis difficult. Substance misuse and withdrawal can lead to psychiatric symptoms, but can also be precipitated by a pre-existing mental health problem. People with co-morbid substance misuse and mental health problems are more likely to have poor medication[223] and treatment[224] compliance. NIMHE is working with the National Treatment Agency on programmes to reduce waiting times and increase access to drug treatment.

Community Drugs Project, Bromley, London

Bromley Community Drugs project (the local branch of Turning Point) works in partnership with Oxleas, South West London and Maudsley NHS Trusts. It focuses on non-opiate users in the community, who are often ignored by statutory services. Most of their client group are crack/cocaine or cannabis users, and 80 per cent have common mental health problems.

The project works closely with, and receives many effective referrals from Oxleas Trust's Assertive Community Team (ACT), which works with clients with complex and multiple needs. Each ACT worker has a small core caseload of ten clients, all of whom are on enhanced CPA. A shared care plan is drawn up between the two agencies and clients, addressing mental health and substance misuse problems simultaneously. In the past year 20 people have signed up to joint care plans and successfully reduced/abstained from substance misuse.

The partnership came from a joint needs assessment in 2001 by substance misuse, mental health and voluntary sector agencies, that resulted in shared assessments and training. The manager of Turning Point described their relationship with the ACT as the *"most effective partnership"* they have.

56. The Department of Health's *Dual Diagnosis Good Practice Guidance* (2002) summarised policy and practice for adults with severe mental health problems and problematic drug use. It clarified that care and support should be provided within mental health services for adults with severe mental health problems.

57. GPs and care staff may not recognise mental health problems among adults with **learning disabilities**, especially if patients have difficulties with communication. *Valuing People: A New Strategy for Learning Disability for the 21st Century* (2001) outlines government plans for people with learning disabilities and their families, including those with mental health problems, to live full and independent lives as part of their communities. There is some evidence that the necessary joint working between health and social care is not always in place for this to happen.[225]

58. GPs receive no payment for people using their practice for less than three months, creating significant disincentives to register **homeless people**, including those in temporary accommodation. This can result in people having to use accident and emergency services. Only one in four rough sleepers is registered with a GP.[226] Following the new General Medical Services contracts, GPs can offer specialist mental health assessments for homeless people. NIMHE is surveying the extent and quality of mental health service contact with homeless people with mental health problems as a baseline for future action.

59. **Prisoners** with severe mental health problems should be transferred to secure mental health facilities, but shortages of specialist facilities can lead to delays. Nearly one in four prisoners accepted for transfer to a community NHS facility waited over three months for it to take place.[227] On release, most prisoners are only given medication for two days, even though many are not registered with a GP and may find it difficult to find a GP. There is little incentive for mainstream mental health services to work with prisons on assessment and resettlement of offenders. People from some ethnic minority groups can be particularly affected by the level of mental healthcare available in the criminal justice system. For example, people from black and ethnic minority communities make up 21 per cent of the male prison population (between two and three times the proportion in the general population).[228]

60. The Correctional Services and Department of Health have a joint target to reduce suicide and self-harm within prisons by 20 per cent by 2010. By 2006, NHS mental health in-reach services will be available in all prisons, with health services commissioned by local primary care trusts. The Prison Service has put in place a suicide prevention strategy, which over the past three years has included:

- investment of over £21 million in a series of interrelated projects;
- recruitment of over 1,200 Samaritan-trained prisoner 'listeners';
- appointment of Suicide Prevention Co-ordinators in the majority of prisons; and
- wider provision of 'safer cells'.

61. The Prison Service is committed to reducing the level of distress in prisons, which has been found to be closely correlated with the suicide rate. Suicide prevention policies are therefore being integrated with other areas such as detoxification, health, purposeful activity and staff and management training. The Prison Service is also determined to ensure that it learns lessons from adverse incidents, and from April 2004, the Prisons and Probation Ombudsman was given responsibility for the investigation of all deaths in custody.

HM Prison Birmingham

The new health centre has two dedicated 17-bed wards for inmates with mental health problems in a general health care setting within the prison. The wards are staffed by health care service personnel, many of whom have worked in community mental health facilities, with a team of prison officers. A primary care team is also based at the health centre. The centre also runs a 60-place 'day centre' facility for inmates with less acute mental health problems and those who are not able to take part in mainstream education facilities. This provides specially designed activities including basic skills work, life skills – such as budgeting – and creative activities.

62. The new National Offender Management Service, bringing together prison and probation services, and the introduction of offender management systems should help improve offenders' access to mainstream mental health services. There is also recognition that, in addition to mental health problems, this group faces multiple barriers to successful re-integration into the community, such as unemployment and homelessness. The Home Office, working closely with other departments, is finalising a national action plan to reduce re-offending, drawing together action on tackling these barriers.

63. There are also a number of valuable schemes to identify mental health problems prior to arrival in prison and divert people into more appropriate provision. Research found that there were around 150 diversion schemes, and that these:

- improved the recognition of mental health problems four-fold;
- cut time from arrest to admission by a factor of seven;
- reduced reconviction rates by half; and
- achieved a successful medical outcome.[229]

64. The majority of people had offended in the context of their mental health problem, having fallen through gaps in community care. Three-quarters had been previously admitted to a psychiatric hospital. However there is no requirement for health or criminal justice agencies to provide diversion schemes and they can be subject to local funding pressures.

65. The Home Office and Department of Health are working together to ensure that the particular mental health needs of **women offenders** are properly met. The *Women's Offending Reduction Programme* and the *Women's Mental Health Strategy* both contain objectives on making community mental health services more appropriate and accessible for women offenders and on reducing the numbers ending up in custody.

66 The Ministry of Defence is developing an evidence-based practical policy on operational stress management in the **armed forces**. This will include prevention, training, better early detection and intervention, and sign-posting to services. There will be a particular focus on stigma and discrimination. In addition, the Ministry is working with the Department of Health to ensure that those who leave the armed forces are aware of NHS arrangements, especially how to access mental health services.

Conclusions

There has been considerable modernisation and investment in mental health services but links between health and social care, employment and other key local partners can be weak. Training on vocational and social issues for health and social care professionals is also limited. Some gaps in service provision remain – such as access to talking therapies and physical health checks. Some groups, such as ethnic minorities or people with complex needs, can face particular barriers to accessing services.

Strengthened advice and support in primary and secondary care should ensure that employment and social issues are addressed early, before they have a detrimental impact. As a result of this report, provision of vocational and social support will be embedded in the Care Programme Approach, with full involvement of the individual. The National Institute for Mental Health in England (NIMHE) will work with the Department for Work and Pensions and the Department for Constitutional Affairs to test models for providing vocational and social support in or linked to primary care.

NIMHE will support health and social care services to transform day services into community resources that promote social inclusion through improved access to mainstream opportunities. It will also work with relevant training organisations to strengthen training on vocational and social issues for health and social care professionals, and tackle inequalities in access to health services.

Chapter 5: Mental health and employment

Summary

- Only 24 per cent of adults with long-term mental health problems are in work. With the right support, many more would be able and would like to work. Unemployment is associated with worsening mental health.
- GPs can have a crucial role in promoting job retention through suggesting work adjustments or referring to a vocational adviser. Occupational health services should support job retention and remove unnecessary barriers to work for people with disabilities or health problems.
- Mental Health Trusts spent £140 million in 2002-03 on day and employment services. The most effective employment projects focus on helping people with mental health problems find work in mainstream settings as quickly as possible, with ongoing support provided as needed. Such projects need not cost more than other employment projects, but can have better outcomes.
- 35 per cent of respondents to the Social Exclusion Unit consultation felt that health and social care services placed a low priority on employment, and only 6 per cent felt it was a high priority.

1. This chapter considers the importance of employment for people with mental health problems, the role of health and social care services in promoting employment, and the scope to improve existing employment support. Chapter 6 looks at barriers to employment, and national initiatives to promote employment and job retention provided by Jobcentre Plus.

Why employment matters

> *"Paid work gives people a real sense of their own value, improves their self-esteem and gets them out of their illness."*

2. People with long-term mental health problems have the lowest employment rate of any of the main groups of disabled people – according to the Labour Force Survey definition, only 24 per cent are currently in work in England.[230] By comparison, research from the US found that with effective rehabilitation support, up to **58 per cent** of adults with severe and enduring mental health problems are able to work using the Individual Placement and Support approach.[231]

Figure 10. Proportion of people by health type who are employed (1998-2003)

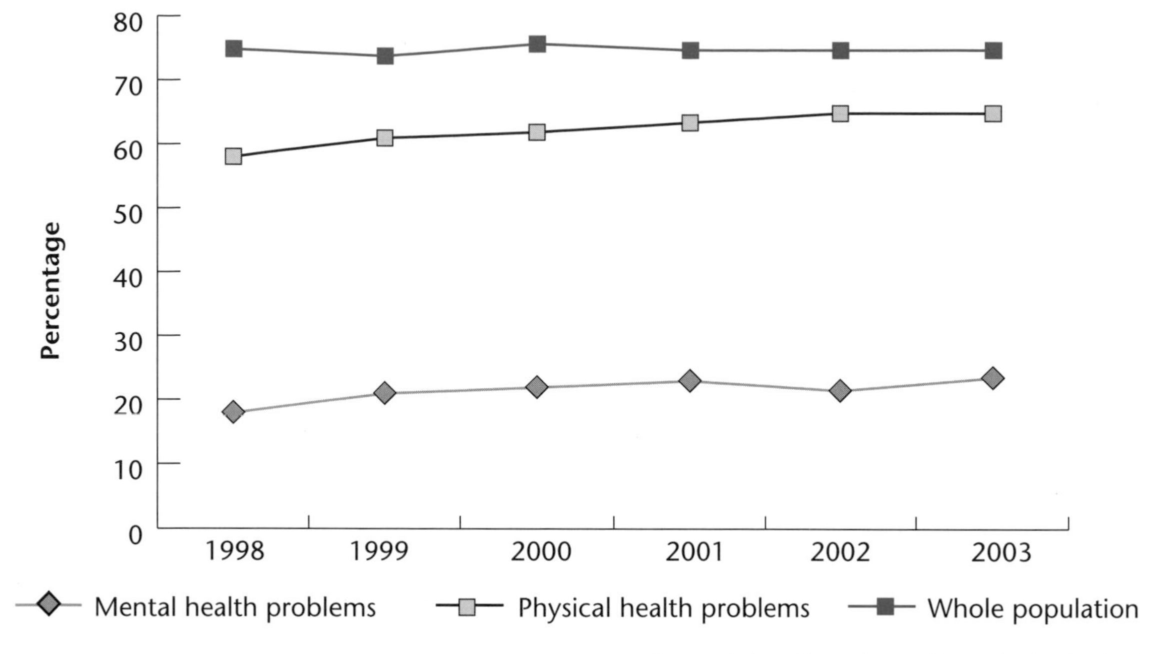

Source: Labour Force Survey, figures for England only.

3. Many people with mental health problems have aspirations to work.[232] Employment can provide a sense of dignity and purpose, financial benefits, and opportunities to meet new people, develop skills, and give something back to the community, all of which boost confidence and self-esteem. People with mental health problems are particularly sensitive to the negative effects of unemployment, and the loss of structure and purpose that it brings.[233]

4. One study found that 48 per cent of people with common mental health problems had had to take time off work.[234] Prolonged unemployment is linked to worsening mental health,[235] whereas having a job can lead to a reduction in symptoms,[236] fewer hospital admissions,[237] and reduced service use.[238]

5. Unemployment can be both a consequence and a cause of mental health problems. There is a strong relationship between unemployment and the development of mental health problems,[239] including an increased risk of suicide.[240] Unemployment is also linked with increased general health problems, including premature death.[241]

The role of GPs and occupational health services in promoting job retention and employment

6. GPs can have a crucial role in facilitating job retention, through suggesting work adjustments or referring to a vocational adviser (as discussed in Chapter 4). Vocational advisers based in primary care can be an accessible source of information on managing the return to work or finding a new job. They can give advice on benefits, liaise with the employee and employer to manage their return, or help with other issues that might impact on work such as housing or financial concerns. Cognitive behavioural therapy and specific work counselling can be useful in the first months of sickness absence.[242]

7. At present, GPs often issue sickness certificates without discussion of other options because of constraints on their time. Evidence suggests that the doctor-patient relationship can be perceived to conflict with the current role of GPs in sickness certification with GPs often making patients' requests a priority and issuing sickness certificates on demand.[243] At least 50 per cent of GPs would rather not have to perform the sickness certification role at all. The research found high levels of variability, with individual GPs judging whether to sign someone off work based not just on their capacity to work but on their age, attitude and job prospects.

8. *Pathways to Work* is a new initiative (described in more detail in Chapter 6) being piloted by the Department for Work and Pensions to help people claiming Incapacity Benefit return to work. As part of *Pathways to Work*, the Department for Work and Pensions and the Department of Health have developed desk aids for GPs outlining the steps to support patients back to work.[244] This includes liaising with employers and Jobcentre Plus offices, and emphasises the importance of early intervention. The Department for Work and Pensions has also produced on-line learning packages for GPs on medical certification and health at work that have been approved for post-graduate accreditation.

9. Just under half of employees have access to an occupational health (OH) service at work, usually those working in the public sector or for large employers. OH services should support job retention and remove unnecessary barriers to work for people with disabilities or health problems. It is important that there is an effective dialogue, with the individual's consent, between GPs and the workplace (including OH services) to ensure that all available support is mobilised to improve job retention and access to employment. The NHS has published guidance for occupational health services on mental health and employment in the NHS.[245]

10. Employers who do not have in-house OH services can purchase it from a number of sources:

- NHS Plus is a network of occupational health services based in NHS hospitals. It provides an occupational health service to NHS staff, and also sells services to the private sector. NHS Plus offers support to industry, commerce and the public sector, with a focus on small and medium enterprises.

- Tailored occupational health support is also available through the Employers' Forum on Disability, the voluntary or private sector. For example, the Samaritans has developed a training package primarily aimed at employees working with external customers who might get angry or upset, but which could also be used by line managers or HR with their own staff.

Safe and Healthy Working Service, Scotland

The Health and Safety Executive is working with partners to set up a series of pilots to provide greater occupational health support for employers. Already running for 18 months, the service is an occupational health service aimed at employers and employees of small and medium enterprises which is funded by the Scottish Executive. It consists of a telephone advice line, a website and a regional network of occupational health and safety advisers. In the first year, 859 calls were received and 148 workplace visits conducted. Callers had generally not taken action to address the issue before contacting the service.

Job Retention and Rehabilitation Pilots

The Department for Work and Pensions, in conjunction with the Department of Health, Health and Safety Executive, Scottish Executive and Welsh Assembly, is running a randomised control trial in six areas. It aims to investigate what helps return to work and job retention for people who have been off work because of sickness, injury or disability, including those with mental health problems. Volunteers, who have been out of work for six to 26 weeks and are at risk of losing their jobs, are randomly assigned to one of four groups. One group offers additional help in the workplace, another assists with healthcare, and the third combines the two. The fourth group is the control group. Evaluation of the pilots will take place in 2005.

Employment support in secondary care

"In 14 years as a service user, mental health professionals have never offered me help with working towards getting back to work."

11. As noted in Chapter 4, in 2002-03, health and social care services spent £140 million on day and employment services for adults with serious mental health problems in England.[246] Anecdotal evidence suggests that adults with mental health problems greatly value the support offered by day services, but that there is scope to make such services more socially inclusive and promote employment better. This section considers the effectiveness of employment support currently offered by health and social care services.

12. Broadly speaking, it is only in recent years that mental health trusts have started to consider employment as a realistic option for people with mental health problems. There is still great variation in available support. 35 per cent of respondents to the Social Exclusion Unit consultation felt that health and social care services placed a low priority on employment, and only 6 per cent felt it was a high priority. Even now, 'vocational services' can too often include a succession of training courses that are designed to fill people's time but do not provide a platform for moving into open employment. However, the best projects bring together key partners to meet clients' health, employment and other needs. They can have a critical role in persuading clients to interact with Jobcentre Plus and overcome fears about benefit loss, both of which can be barriers to work (discussed in more detail in Chapter 6).

Employment support, South West London and St George's Mental Health NHS Trust

Since 1995, the Trust has successfully increased its employment rate for people with severe and enduring mental health problems, with over 100 people being employed on the same terms and conditions as other staff.[247] Evaluation suggests that each person employed in this way saved the government **£1900** per year in reduced welfare spending and higher taxes, not including healthcare savings. [248]

The Trust has developed a Vocational Services Strategy based on the Individual Placement and Support approach (see below). Occupational therapists and borough mental health and employment co-ordinators work within the clinical teams to enable people with severe mental health problems to access open employment and mainstream education. Ongoing support is included in care plans, with a focus on individual choice. In 2002, the Trust supported 161 people in open employment, 97 in voluntary work and 182 in mainstream education or training.

The early intervention team includes a part-time vocational specialist to co-ordinate vocational plans with the individual and the clinical team, help people to find and keep jobs and education courses, and provide access to benefits advice. After one year, the employment rate rose from 10 per cent to 40 per cent, and the percentage not engaged in education, training or employment dropped from 55 per cent to 5 per cent.[249]

The Trust has begun to implement the Individual Placement and Support approach within the community mental health teams through integrating an employment specialist into community mental health teams. In addition, vocational outcomes have been negotiated with commissioners as a Key Performance Indicator for the Trust.

13. Health and social care services can provide employment support directly or commission them from the voluntary, community or private sectors. Employment support might be provided in traditional day centres, specialist employment facilities, or mainstream community settings. At a national level, help with finding employment is provided by Jobcentre Plus, described in more detail in Chapter 6. To maximise employment opportunities, Jobcentre Plus and health and social care staff need to work in partnership together – for example Disability Employment Advisers in Jobcentre Plus could forge links with the new mental health workers described in Chapter 4.

Making Space – Options, Stafford

Making Space is a voluntary organisation working with people with severe and enduring mental health problems. Its Stafford office, Making Space – Options, offers support to clients to return to work through use of a logbook detailing the necessary steps to employment. This includes identifying goals, developing a CV, and providing benefits advice. A key factor contributing to successful delivery has been close working with local partners, including Jobcentre Plus and the local college. For example, based on clients' feedback, Making Space – Options worked with Jobcentre Plus to agree a new format for clients' meetings with Disability Employment Advisers so that clients were better able to understand the options open to them.

Making Space – Options piloted a pre-access to employment programme for clients needing additional support before using the logbook. 26 people took part, of whom nine were seeking work. They were encouraged to be open about their mental health problems when applying for jobs. Despite initial concerns about employer prejudice, eight have since found work, and the ninth is waiting for the results of an interview. Three of the others are starting self-employment, and 13 have completed computer courses relating to employment training.

"You are programmed in life and pre-conditioned to do a job for 40 hours a week, but this made me realise I could do what I want to do, which is two part-time jobs."

14. There is a range of models of employment support in England.

- Many mental health trusts and social care services still commission or provide **sheltered workshops**, which have high staffing levels and typically offer a limited range of unskilled activities and few opportunities for career progression. Wages can be below national minimum wage levels (recent guidance from the Department for Trade and Industry identified the situations where this was possible). [250]

- **'Train and place'** models, where the individual has a long period of vocational training, voluntary work and/or work experience before attempting paid employment.

- **Social firms** create employment in a supported setting for disabled people (primarily with mental health problems or learning disabilities), while trading on the open market. Social Firms UK aims to increase employment opportunities for disabled people through the development of social firms.

Six Mary's Place Guesthouse, Edinburgh

Six Mary's Place Guesthouse was set up by Forth Sector in Edinburgh after research identified a need for flexible, supported employment for people with mental health problems. It has 22 participants, most of whom are trainees, training for 8-16 hours per week in return for a weekly training allowance of up to £20. It also has four full-time paid staff, two of whom have experience of mental health problems. The guesthouse offers different opportunities to trainees to fit in with their needs – for example, if someone found it difficult to get up in the morning because of their medication, they could work as a housekeeper during the middle of the day.

Six Mary's Place was refurbished in the late 1990s so that all rooms are now en-suite. 80 per cent of its income is from sales, and it usually has full occupancy (dropping to 80 per cent occupancy in low season).

"You've no idea what it means to be able to say, 'I'm working'."

- **Intermediate labour markets (ILMs)** help people gain employment skills and provide a bridge back to work by offering fixed-term contracts (often up to 12 months) together with training, jobsearch help and personal development activities. They are usually aimed at people who are most removed from the labour market, which can include those with mental health problems.

- **Supported employment** has a primary aim of immediate jobsearch and help finding mainstream employment, with ongoing support such as help with a CV or benefits advice provided as needed.

- **Individual Placement and Support (IPS)** projects for people with severe mental health problems are similar to supported employment, but with a greater emphasis on integrating health and vocational support. They provide unlimited ongoing support once someone starts work.

Individual Placement and Support

The Individual Placement and Support (IPS) approach is evidence-based and built on six key principles:

- finding employment in integrated/mainstream settings ('real work');
- immediate jobsearch, with minimal pre-vocational training;
- support from vocational workers based in clinical teams, with employment an integral part of the overall care plan;
- jobsearch driven by client preferences and choice;
- continual assessment of individuals' needs, with support adjusted as necessary and assistance in career progression; and
- access to ongoing support on a time-unlimited basis once in work, with appropriate workplace interventions to enable job retention.

Following a systematic review of vocational rehabilitation for people with severe and enduring mental health problems,[251] there is strong evidence of the effectiveness of the IPS approach over other methods in enabling people with severe mental health problems to work. The IPS model was developed in the US, but early evaluation of IPS projects in the UK suggests that the approach could be used without further adaptation in the UK.[252]

15. The extent to which different schemes operate in the UK is not well understood, in part because different projects open and close all the time. One study in the North West of England found high variation in provision and a poor relationship between the schemes identified and the needs of the areas in which they operated.[253] In that research, the highest level of provision of places was in the area with the lowest deprivation and unemployment levels.

16. A **cost-effectiveness study** commissioned for the Social Exclusion Unit concluded that **supported employment** and **Individual Placement and Support** projects were significantly more effective than other approaches in enabling people with mental health problems to find and keep open employment.[254] Converting less effective programmes to supported employment could be cost-saving, or at least cost-neutral for local services and the government, and would have broader social benefits.

17. US research compared vocational and non-vocational outcomes of day centres and supported employment projects.[255] Client employment rates in the day centre remained constant at 5 per cent per month but in day centres converted to supported employment programmes, they rose to between 15 and 35 per cent per month.

18. People with mental health problems need a **range of employment options**, as individual needs vary. Some will not be able to work in the open labour market, and will continue to need alternative work opportunities. However, evidence suggests that many more, currently denied the opportunity, could benefit from active support to find work and are capable of moving into work quickly without extensive training.

First Step Trust, Lambeth, London

First Step Trust Lambeth is a small, not-for-profit community business, which is staffed and managed by people with severe and enduring mental health problems and other difficulties. It aims to support individuals to gain control of their lives through work and paid employment. It offers a variety of services including gardening, painting and decorating, caretaking and printing. Each section runs as a small business, trading with the local community (NHS trusts, local authorities and the private sector), with everyone at the project encouraged to share in running the business. In Clapham, FST Abbevilles restaurant provides training and employment in a restaurant that is open to the public.

Nationally, the First Step Trust organisation has a turnover of more than £1.4 million per year with 600 workforce members attending 16 projects across the country in the course of a year. Most workers are on benefits, gaining experience and confidence to return to paid employment. One-third of the salaried positions are held by staff who started as members of that volunteer workforce.

Conclusion

Many people with mental health problems want to work. Unemployment is associated with worsening mental health. Health and social care services have an important role in promoting employment, and currently provide a range of employment services, particularly in secondary care. GPs and occupational health services can have a crucial role in promoting job retention, working with individuals and their employers.

There is significant scope to improve current provision by using existing funding to convert less effective programmes into Individual Placement and Support projects or other forms of supported employment. This would bring broader social benefits as well as reduced healthcare costs. As a result of this report, the National Institute for Mental Health in England, in liaison with the Department for Work and Pensions, will work with health and social care services to implement evidence-based practice, in particular the Individual Placement and Support approach.

CHAPTER 6: Overcoming barriers to employment

Summary

- Barriers to employment include low confidence, low expectations among staff, employer attitudes, and difficulties moving from benefits to work. There can also be a lack of support to help people retain jobs.
- The number of people on Incapacity Benefit for mental health reasons has grown significantly in recent years. More people claim Incapacity Benefit and Severe Disablement Allowance for mental health reasons than claim Jobseekers' Allowance.
- Jobcentre Plus has a number of initiatives to help people with disabilities to find work. In October 2003, it began piloting its flagship programme to transform Incapacity Benefit, *Pathways to Work.*

1. People claiming Incapacity Benefit (IB) for mental health reasons are more likely to be away from the labour market for longer,[256] and are more at risk of leaving employment than people with other disabilities.[257] The previous chapter considered the benefits of employment for mental health, and the help that health and social care services can provide to support employment. This chapter looks at the barriers to employment and national initiatives to promote employment and job retention.

Judith's story – overcoming barriers to employment

Judith was first admitted to hospital with depression while she was training to be a psychiatric nurse, and was off work for three months. Her colleagues were very supportive, and she was able to complete her studies six months later than everyone else. She later qualified as a registered mental health nurse.

In 1992, she was offered a job on an adolescent unit in a different town, but the post was later withdrawn *"on the advice of our occupational health department"*. Her GP – whom she had never met – had supplied a medical report, getting many key facts wrong, and not stating that her mental health problems were six years ago and her life had moved on. Her husband wanted her to pursue a discrimination case, but she couldn't face it and continued to work full-time at her old hospital.

Her mental health problems recurred four years later after the birth of her son, but despite several hospital admissions, she was able to continue working part-time between relapses and was promoted to day hospital sister.

"Despite everything, I'm not ashamed of my mental health problems. I think they've played a significant part in making me the person I am today."

Barriers to employment

2. There are a number of reasons why people with mental health problems have difficulties finding or keeping a job.

- **The impact of the mental health problems on the individual**, leading to loss of motivation and confidence. Side effects of some medication (such as drowsiness) can rule out certain jobs.

- **Fear that work will lead to worsening mental health**, even though unemployment is actually likely to be more detrimental to mental health.

- **Low expectations of staff**. Lack of understanding about the benefits of employment can lead health and social care staff to advise against work. Jobcentre Plus staff can have poor awareness of mental health issues. This can lead to a culture of low expectations, with the assumption that some individuals will 'never' be able to work.[258]

- **Employer attitudes**. Many employers are reluctant to employ people with mental health problems, as discussed in Chapter 3. Occupational health departments might also raise concerns that the individual would be unable to cope or would take too much time off sick.

- **People with mental health problems lacking awareness about available support**. There appears to be low usage of Jobcentre Plus among people with mental health problems, who may not be aware of recent initiatives to ease the transition to work.

- **Benefit reviews**. Although automatic benefit reviews are not the policy of the Department for Work and Pensions, there is a widespread fear that looking for work, including unpaid work, will trigger a benefits review. Similar concerns occur about Disability Living Allowance (DLA), although this can be paid to those in or out of work. DLA is discussed further in Chapter 8.

- **Financial implications of leaving benefits**.[259] Many people feel that leaving benefits represents a real threat to their financial security. They have concerns either that they would be worse off in work, or that the job would not work out and they would need to reclaim their whole benefits package, which might have been difficult to secure in the first place. People claiming through their health insurance fear having higher premiums or being unable to get health insurance in future if they return to work. Action to address these issues includes the Working Tax Credit, which tops up the wages of people on low incomes working for 16 hours or more, and the linking rules for people on benefits.

The benefits system

What are the 'linking rules'?

People who leave Incapacity Benefit to move into work or training, and reclaim the benefit within one year for the same health condition, will **re-qualify for the same level of benefit**. This extends to **two years** (104 weeks) if they were eligible for the Working Tax Credit disability premium when in work. Claimants have to register by telephone or in writing within one month of leaving benefit to qualify for the linking rules.

Linking rules apply differently to Housing Benefit (HB) and Council Tax Benefit. In 2002, a shortened claim form was introduced for people **reclaiming HB within 12 weeks** of leaving the benefit for those who had previously been claiming Jobseekers' Allowance or Income Support.

3. Anecdotal evidence suggests that **the linking rules are not widely understood**. The 12-week reclaim process for Housing Benefit, while welcomed as a step in the right direction, has been criticised for being too short. People who return to benefits using the linking rules have to spend a further **28 weeks on benefit to become eligible** for the linking rules again, even if they could move into employment more quickly.

The Permitted Work rules

There is evidence that helping people with mental health problems to **increase their hours gradually** can improve their employment prospects.[260] 'Permitted work' aims to bridge the gap between benefits and full-time work by enabling people to work for up to 16 hours per week and remain on benefits.

Incapacity Benefit claimants are allowed to earn up to a fixed amount, either at the **higher** level (£72 per week for up to a year depending on progress towards full-time employment) or **lower** level (£20 per week for an indefinite period). **Supported permitted work** allows claimants to earn up to £72 per week for an indefinite period if receiving a recognised form of support while in work, such as working in a social firm.

There is provision under the permitted work rules for **averaging hours** over a period to establish whether the hours worked in a week are within the 16 hour limit. There is also scope for averaging earnings to establish a weekly amount where they are not paid on a weekly basis.

People claiming Income Support, Housing Benefit or Council Tax Benefit in addition to Incapacity Benefit can still earn up to £72 per week, but these benefits will be reduced for earnings over £20. Income Support will be reduced by the equivalent amount earned above £20, so if someone earns £25, IS will be reduced by £5. The net gain for working will remain at £20. If someone is not claiming IS (or has finished claiming IS), but is claiming Housing and Council Tax Benefits, these will be reduced by 85p in total[261] for every additional pound earned above the earnings disregard limits.

4. 44 per cent of IB claimants also claim Income Support and can only earn £20 before losing benefits (equivalent to around four hours' work at national minimum wage levels). Meetings with people with mental health problems suggest they either believe they are restricted to four hours' work, or are put off by knowing that they will not gain more than £20 for up to 16 hours' work and the need to have benefits recalculated. As such, there is a perceived gap between four and 16 hours' work, the point at which people become eligible for Working Tax Credit.

5. **Delays recalculating benefit entitlements** when people start work, particularly for housing and council tax benefits, can lead to debt when the local authority tries to claim back overpaid benefits.

> **Changes to Housing and Council Tax Benefits**
>
> From April 2004, people claiming Incapacity Benefit and Severe Disablement Allowance will continue to receive Housing and Council Tax Benefit for the first four weeks after starting work, to help bridge the gap between benefits and the first wage cheque. In addition, the majority of HB claimants no longer have to make a new claim upon starting work. The Department for Work and Pensions is also working with local authorities to improve the speed of processing claims.

Sickness and disability benefits claimant rates

6. 35 per cent of people coming onto Incapacity Benefit cite mental health problems as their main disability, up from 22 per cent in 1995. The number of people claiming IB because of mental health problems has **almost doubled** over this period, from 475,000 in 1995 to 848,000 now, with a further 58,200 people claiming Severe Disablement Allowance (SDA).[262] This does not include those with secondary mental health problems or who develop mental health problems while on IB. More people claim IB and SDA for mental health reasons than the total number of Jobseekers' Allowance claimants.[263]

Figure 11: IB and SDA beneficiaries with mental health problems, as a proportion of the population

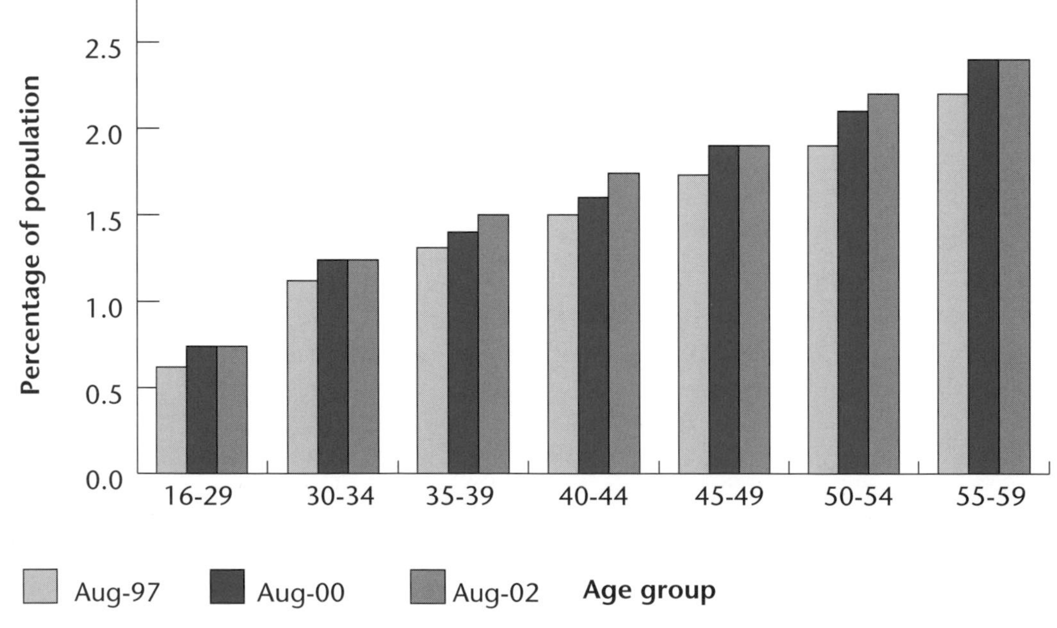

Data source: IB Admin Data.

7. The proportion of people claiming sickness and disability benefits with mental health problems increases with age, and at a faster rate than the general prevalence for mental health problems (discussed in Chapter 1). One possible reason for the increase is the labour market conditions for older people. Nationally, one-third of people aged between 50 and 65 are not in work,[264] most of whom did not volunteer to leave work early.[265]

8. Claimant rates for incapacity benefits vary across the country, with a significantly higher proportion of people claiming for mental health problems in the North East and North West than elsewhere in the country. This may be driven by higher rates of worklessness and the decline of traditional industries in these areas. The forthcoming Social Exclusion Unit report on *Jobs and Enterprise in Deprived Areas* will set out evidence on the local areas still suffering from very high levels of worklessness, and what more government plans to do about them.

Figure 12: Percentage of people claiming sickness and disability benefits for mental health problems by region

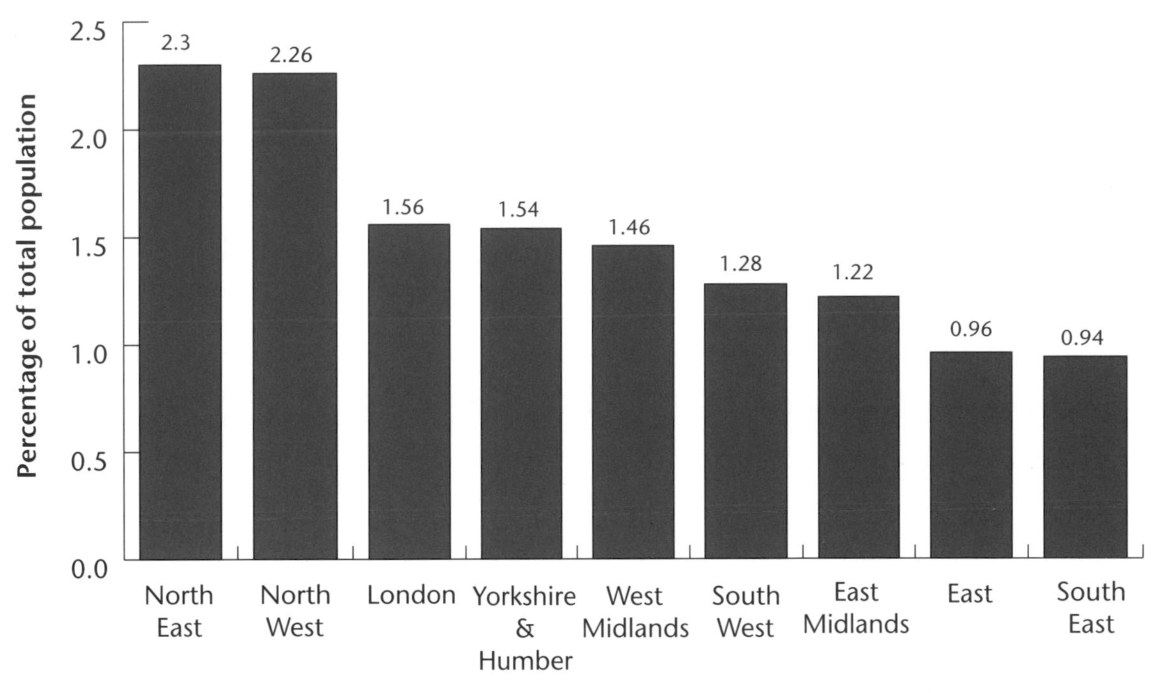

Data source: IB Admin Data, August 2003.

9. In addition to those claiming sickness and disability benefits, an unknown number of people claiming Jobseekers' Allowance also have mental health problems. Jobcentre Plus staff have no medical information about these clients, which can make it difficult to refer them to appropriate provision.

Pentreath Ltd, Cornwall

Pentreath Ltd is a voluntary sector organisation that provides a range of routes into employment for adults with mental health problems, from sheltered work places to helping people secure open paid employment for those who are work ready. It receives funding from the health and employment sectors and has a contract with Jobcentre Plus to deliver individual needs assessments and confidence building. Support and financial incentives are also provided to employers where necessary.

Employment rates for particular groups

10. Some people with mental health problems face additional barriers to employment. **Lone parents** with mental health problems are over **three times less likely to be employed** than those without.[266] Evaluation of the New Deal for Lone Parents has shown that those without health problems were more likely to take part and benefit from the programme.[267] A lack of access to childcare can also hinder parents' return to work.

11. There is little data about employment rates for people from **ethnic minorities** with mental health problems. However, only 58 per cent of the working-age ethnic minority population is in work compared to 75 per cent of the working-age population as a whole.[268] Anecdotal evidence from Social Exclusion Unit visits suggests that people from ethnic minorities with mental health problems face double-discrimination in the labour market on grounds of race and disability. In addition, they can be under-represented in specialist mental health employment schemes.[269]

12. The Department for Work and Pensions and the PPP Foundation co-sponsored a report, *Hidden Skills, Hidden Talents*,[270] which explored ways of helping people with mental health problems from ethnic minority groups into employment. A video, *Better Must Come*, highlighting some of the issues raised in the report, especially the aspirations of young Black African and Caribbean men, has been developed by the Mellow Campaign and the Sainsbury Centre for Mental Health, and funded by The Square Mile, the Department for Work and Pensions, and the London Borough of Newham.

13. **Younger** and **older** people often face more barriers to entering the labour market. Young people who develop mental health problems while still in education might miss out on gaining necessary skills and qualifications for work.[271] Connexions advisers offer specialist support to young people aged 13-19 to help them make the transition to adult life, discussed further in Chapter 8. As noted earlier, the proportion of older people claiming benefits is higher than the general population.

14. People with **complex needs**, such as homelessness, substance misuse or learning disabilities in addition to their mental health problems can also face a double disadvantage when trying to find work. Yet work (paid or unpaid) can be a key route out of homelessness, and help to prevent homelessness. The Office of the Deputy Prime Minister funds a range of projects across the country that provide support, training and work experience for homeless people, many of whom have had or are still experiencing mental health problems.

Initiatives to help people find employment

Outreach and partnership working between agencies

15. There is increasing evidence that marketing and delivering employment support in a range of settings can improve employment rates for people with mental health problems.[272] Increased partnership working between Jobcentre Plus offices, health and social care organisations, and the voluntary sector would create greater opportunities for people to seek employment support from organisations that they know and trust.[273] This would also allow organisations to see the individual's employment needs in the context of their health, housing and social needs, and work to address barriers to employment that were not work related. The forthcoming Social Exclusion Unit report on *Jobs and Enterprise in Deprived Areas* will include proposals on outreach for clients with complex needs. The benefits of outreach for clients with multiple disadvantages have also emerged from the Social Exclusion Unit's *Impacts and Trends* project. The lessons learned by *Impact and Trends* in relation to outreach, and a range of other delivery issues, are informing the Department for Work and Pensions' strategy for helping the most disadvantaged clients.

BEAT – Action Teams for Jobs, Bodmin, Cornwall

BEAT is part of Jobcentre Plus. It employs two full-time members of staff and has a joint caseload of 132 people. It uses community outreach to try to change community perceptions of Jobcentre Plus and the support it can offer. Through BEAT, clients also have access to a debt counsellor once a month, a housing advice officer, and staff at St Petrocs, a local charity and hostel that works with homeless people, once a week. It has funding to provide flexible support to meet individual needs – team members can authorise purchases up to £300 or put a business case to head office for higher amounts.

The team spends one day a week at Bodmin psychiatric hospital, to discuss people's options when they leave hospital, and help make the transition less intimidating. The team is also part of a more general community outreach service, which provides advice weekly on housing benefits, pensions and adult education in Bodmin town centre.

Jobcentre Plus

16. The government has invested heavily in helping people with health conditions and disabilities to find work. *Pathways to Work* is designed to transform work opportunities for people making a claim for Incapacity Benefit. It has been piloted in three areas since October 2003, and a further four areas since April 2004.

Pathways to Work

Key features of *Pathways to Work* include:

- A **new team of skilled personal advisers** within Jobcentre Plus focusing solely on Incapacity Benefit clients and trained in health/disability awareness, influencing and motivating clients.
- **Six mandatory monthly work-focused meetings** for most new IB clients to discuss work options (including support to help return to work), explain IB rules and medical tests, and develop an action plan. Personal advisers have discretion to delay repeat IB reviews where an individual is starting to look for work.
- A **voluntary 'Choices' package**, combining existing provision (described below) and new Condition Management Programmes delivered jointly between Jobcentre Plus and the NHS. These are cognitive education programmes that aim to help clients understand and better manage their condition in a work environment so that they are more confident about returning to work and negotiating with their employer about their needs. The programmes are being designed and commissioned by primary care trusts in the pilot areas.
- **Financial incentives**, including a **Return to Work credit of £40 per week**, and access to the **Advisers' Discretion Fund**.

17. In addition to *Pathways to Work* support for new Incapacity Benefit claimants, new measures for people who have been claiming IB for up to **two years** were proposed in Budget 2004, and will be piloted from 2005 in *Pathways to Work* areas. These include mandatory work-focused interviews, and a job preparation premium of £20 for existing IB claimants undertaking relevant work-related activity.

18. *Pathways to Work* will incorporate existing Jobcentre Plus initiatives to promote employment for disabled people. These include:

- a **work-focused interview** for new Incapacity Benefit claimants in all Jobcentre Plus offices;
- 600 **Disability Employment Advisers** within Jobcentre Plus offering additional support to people with disabilities;
- **WORKSTEP**, which offers job support to disabled people with complex work-related barriers. It provides opportunities to work in a supportive environment and progress to mainstream employment. Providers aim to influence employers' perceptions of employing disabled people;

Enable project, Shropshire

The Enable Disability Employment Team, part of Shropshire's mental health services, is funded by Shropshire County Council and the Shropshire Primary Care NHS Trust, and has a WORKSTEP contract with Jobcentre Plus. It can provide higher levels of support to people with severe and enduring mental health problems over a longer time period than is usual for WORKSTEP. It acts as a bridge between health and social care clinical teams and Jobcentre Plus, so that health and social care, through Enable, can provide ongoing support once people have left WORKSTEP.

The team provides advice, guidance and support to jobseekers and employers. Its mental health job retention service provides a mediation and advice service between employees with mental health problems and their employers. Between June 2002 and May 2004, Enable helped 132 people into paid work, 63 into voluntary work, 48 into education and training and had 101 successful job retention outcomes.

- the **New Deal for Disabled People**, which offers support for people on incapacity benefits to move into work through a network of job brokers. Tailored help includes a personal back to work plan, help in effective job search skills, and in-work support where needed for up to 26 weeks after starting a job; and
- **Access to Work**, which provides individually tailored support to remove disability-related barriers that would otherwise prevent take up or continuation of work. An estimated 5 per cent of Access to Work clients have mental health problems, the fourth largest group of claimants.[274]

19. In May 2004, the Department for Work and Pensions published a preliminary paper, *Building on New Deal: Local solutions meeting individual needs.*[275] The paper outlines a strategy to build on the success of the New Deal, strengthening its ability to help Jobcentre Plus clients facing particular difficulties moving into employment and simplifying its administration. It will offer a more personalised approach, with personal advisers and local managers having sufficient flexibility to deliver solutions appropriate for individuals and local labour markets. The full paper will be published shortly.

20. Jobcentre Plus's **employer engagement strategy** aims to develop a better understanding of, and focus on employers' needs, to encourage more employers to use Jobcentre Plus and provide a greater range of employment opportunities for clients.

The business case for employing people with mental health problems

"Companies that do not embrace diversity, including disability, as a core business issue, are simply missing the point."

(Sir Peter Bonfield, Chief Executive, BT plc)[276]

"To support our staff when mental health goes wrong means that we support them in the whole of their lives, which in turn means we get the best out of them at work."

(Annie Ralph, Chief Executive, Braintree District Council)[277]

- Mental health problems affect up to one in six adults at any one time. No employer can afford to ignore such a large group of potential employees. People with mental health problems have a range of skills and talents that can fill gaps in the labour market.
- Many adults develop mental health problems during their careers. Enabling people to stay in work makes much better business sense than paying for medical retirement and recruiting new staff. The typical additional costs of ill health retirement and replacement recruitment in the public sector are around £100,000.[278]
- People with mental health problems are keen to work and are committed employees. For example, adults with mental health problems employed by South West London and St George's Mental Health Trust have lower sickness absence rates than the Trust's workforce as a whole (3.8 per cent, compared to 5.8 per cent across the Trust as a whole).[279]
- Workplace adjustments are likely to be straightforward, such as flexibility in working hours (as for lone parents), and are typically very low cost – US research found that 90 per cent cost less than $100.[280]
- Employers have legal duties under the Disability Discrimination Act 1995 not to discriminate against disabled employees and job applicants, including people whose mental health problems results in them being disabled.
- Good management practices will also help prevent and reduce the impact of mental health problems developing among other employees, and minimise sickness absence.

21. At present, Jobcentre Plus programmes are not always able to meet the particular needs of people with mental health problems. For example, WORKSTEP requires people to work for 16 or more hours per week, and Access to Work requires a stable health condition, both of which may rule out people with mental health problems. The Department for Work and Pensions is considering greater tailoring of provision to meet individual needs, which should help meet the needs of this client group more effectively.

National Employment Panel: *A New Deal for All*

The National Employment Panel's recent report, *A New Deal for All,* recommends a number of substantial changes to Jobcentre Plus's New Deal programmes.[281] These are aimed at increasing the effectiveness of programmes for people who are most socially excluded. Of particular relevance to mental health issues are proposed changes to:

- *the initial assessment of clients:* so that those with multiple barriers are identified earlier and provided with more intensive support;
- *the way success is measured:* both to place a greater emphasis on job retention and to reward providers for increasing someone's job readiness i.e. recognising the 'distance travelled';
- *the procurement and contracting system:* to promote greater use of specialist providers; and
- *the emphasis placed on local employer engagement:* to increase the number of suitable work placements and job opportunities.

Job retention and sustainability

"There will often be a lack of support when things start to go wrong, often no help to retain jobs or adapt jobs to avoid stressors. People often talk about being isolated from colleagues and unable to talk up about the difficulties they're having."

22. People with mental health problems can face difficulties retaining their old job or sustaining a new job. As noted in Chapter 5, GPs can play a crucial role in promoting job retention but do not always have the time to discuss alternatives to issuing sickness certificates. Other barriers to job retention can include a stressful work environment and a lack of support for employers and employees.

Establishing a healthy workplace

23. Approximately two-thirds of people with mental health problems believe that unrealistic workloads, long hours and bad management caused or exacerbated their mental health problems.[282] The British Occupational Health Research Foundation is funding an evidence review on managing mental health problems in the workplace, which will result in the development of evidence-based guidelines.

24. The Health and Safety Executive, in partnership with 22 public and private sector employers, is developing and piloting management standards against which performance can be judged. A tool to record and measure sickness absence, and best practice guidance on managing sickness absence and supporting people back to work, will be launched in summer 2004. These will be particularly aimed at small and medium enterprises (SMEs).

25. In addition to promoting a generally healthy working environment, employers have a duty to make 'reasonable adjustments' for disabled employees under the Disability Discrimination Act (1995).

Promoting job retention, BT

BT has implemented a number of measures to ensure reasonable adjustments are made and has seen positive results. The company stresses the need for flexible working for people who have identified the 'trigger factors' known to increase their risk of mental health problems. For example, individuals have been enabled to work reduced hours, and they have improved telephone conferencing to allow people to work from home. This approach has resulted in a decrease of 80 per cent in early retirement rates for people with mental health problems.

The role of the manager and support for employers

> *"Many line managers are confused and fearful about engaging with a person who is experiencing mental distress. They worry that they will say the wrong thing or that they will open a can of worms that they have neither the time nor experience to handle."* [283]

26. Research involving 1596 employees in a range of companies found that only 20 per cent were confident they could manage someone with mental health problems effectively, yet 70 per cent of managers had had to manage someone with a diagnosed mental health problem.[284]

27. The lack of support for managers or employers when an employee has mental health problems can be a particular concern for SMEs. SMEs rarely have a dedicated HR or occupational health section, and can lack advice about mental health issues. They can also lack the financial capacity to keep a job open for extended periods if an employee is off sick.

28. *Mindout* published *A line manager's resource: a practical guide to managing mental health in the workplace* covering recruitment, early intervention, keeping in touch during sickness absence and managing the return to work.[285] Occupational health services can also provide support to line managers, as discussed in Chapter 5.

Support for employees

29. Employer support for employees can include 'buddying' schemes, welfare and occupational health services, or job coaching. Some people may need external ongoing support. This can also involve liaising with the employer to raise awareness and provide advice on reasonable adjustments. People with mental health problems frequently do not want colleagues to know their situation, so unlike people with learning disabilities, having someone sit with them in the workplace would not always be appropriate.

Job Retention Team, Avon and Wiltshire

The Job Retention Team began as a pilot funded by the Department for Work and Pensions and the Avon and Wiltshire Mental Health Partnership. Following a needs' assessment, clients are offered counselling, anxiety management, goal setting and confidence building. The team liaises with employers, advising on a gradual return to work, reasonable adjustments and DDA obligations. It also offers mental health awareness training. Clients and employers can have ongoing support once back at work. If it is not appropriate for clients to return to the original job, support is offered to find a new job or to retrain.

30. Various Jobcentre Plus initiatives, such as *Pathways to Work*, WORKSTEP and the New Deal for Disabled People, offer ongoing support for clients once in work. For example, the New Deal for Disabled People offers support for up to 26 weeks once a client has started work, and support is available for 6-12 months through *Pathways to Work*. Time-unlimited support is a key feature of Individual Placement and Support projects supported by health and social care services.

Career progression

"At present, the glass ceiling that women have identified is more like a concrete ceiling for mental health service users: many of us cannot even see through to the possibility of senior roles or wider influence." [286]

"The reality frequently is of having to take on low paid work with few prospects where they may be financially worse off and be in a lower status job than previously."

31. Adults with mental health problems who find work tend to take jobs with lower rates of pay and responsibility than they had before their health problems started. A recent study reported that two-thirds of people with mental health problems returning to work had less responsibility, worked fewer hours and were paid much less.[287] This can have a negative effect on a person's health through being under-employed and having limited control over their work. On average, people with severe and enduring mental health problems who manage to find employment earn only two-thirds of the national average hourly rate.[288]

32. There is a lack of research about opportunities for progression in employment for people with mental health problems. Anecdotal evidence from meetings with people with mental health problems suggests that the culture of low expectations can lead to people not progressing beyond entry level jobs. Some projects, for example, those using the Individual Placement and Support approach, include a focus on career progression.

Self-employment and enterprise

33. For some people with mental health problems, self-employment and enterprise may present the most practical means of re-entering the labour market. It can enable people to work in a way that fits around their mental health condition and avoids problems of disclosure and employer discrimination. In discussions with the Social Exclusion Unit, people from ethnic minorities have stressed the value of enterprise as a potential route back to work.

34. The government is committed to encouraging more enterprise in disadvantaged communities and among groups who may face particular difficulties setting up their own business. The Phoenix Development Fund aims to find innovative ways of providing business support to people in disadvantaged areas and those groups under-represented in business ownership, including people with disabilities. People with mental health problems have been identified as one of the groups to be supported through the second phase of the fund (2004-06).

35. In 2003, the Small Business Service commissioned Social Firms UK and Mind to identify how enterprise could support people with mental health problems. Recommendations included: better information for mental health professionals and clients about employment, including self-employment; improving links between mental health agencies and business support organisations; and promoting intermediate labour markets or social firms as a way of providing long and short-term employment.

Conclusion

Finding and retaining employment is one of the most important and difficult issues facing people with mental health problems. People need a wider range of employment opportunities and help to overcome barriers to work from both health and social care services and Jobcentre Plus. The Department for Work and Pensions has introduced changes to the employment and benefits system to help people move into work, but these are not always well understood.

Following this report, and depending on successful evaluation results and availability of funding, the government will work towards roll-out of the *Pathways to Work* Incapacity Benefit pilots, and improve employment support through other employment programmes. Action will be taken to ease the transition from benefits to work, and raise awareness of recent employment and benefits changes. There will also be additional support for employers, and new funding to promote enterprise and self-employment.

CHAPTER 7: Supporting families and community participation

Summary

- Many people have reduced contact with family and friends following the onset of mental health problems, and a significant minority find their social networks become restricted to people within mental health services.
- Mental health problems can have a major emotional and financial impact on families, which can lead to carers developing mental health problems themselves. Greater awareness in adult mental health services of children's needs will help services work more supportively with parents who have mental health problems and can improve children's emotional and mental well-being.
- Being a volunteer or taking on community roles such as being a school governor can increase the opportunities to interact with the local community. People with mental health problems can also benefit from activities such as education, arts or sports.
- Community-based activities can develop skills, raise confidence, and boost employment opportunities as well as being an end in themselves. Some people will need support to participate fully in mainstream activities.

The importance of social networks

"Mental health problems are lonely illnesses – it's the quickest way I know to lose all the people who aren't paid to care for you. You need people to be with you, to stick by you, to talk about something other than what's going on inside your head. If you've got someone like that, you've got a good chance."

1. Families and friends play a critical role in promoting the well-being of people with mental health problems. However, these relationships can be affected by mental health problems. Adults with common mental health problems are more likely to have an unmet desire to participate more fully in family and social activities than those with no mental health problems.[289]

- People with a psychotic disorder are three times more likely to be divorced than those without.[290]
- One survey found the social networks of four out of ten people with mental health problems living in the community were restricted to people within mental health services.[291]
- Research with over 3,000 people with severe mental health problems found that even among those in contact with support organisations, a quarter had no or very limited involvement with community activities. [292]
- A recent survey found that 84 per cent of people with mental health problems have felt isolated compared with 29 per cent of the general population[293]. Young people, ethnic minorities and people in rural communities were likely to be the most isolated.

2. Participation rates in arts, sports and leisure activities among adults with mental health problems are not currently well documented. However, there is evidence that people with mental health problems (particularly severe and enduring mental health problems) often are less occupied than those without. Adults with common mental health problems are less likely to belong to a sports club or social club than those without.[294]

3. Over half the respondents to the Social Exclusion Unit consultation highlighted the importance of social networks and social activities. Activities such as studying or volunteering can help boost employment chances, as well as being a valuable end in themselves.

> *"[I would like] to be able to afford to go out and meet understanding people. On a low income, it is very stressful to live."*

4. Social networks can be important in enabling people with mental health problems to access opportunities in the community. This might be through emotional support – having someone to talk to and rely on at times of need – or practical help with issues like benefits, transport or childcare. The level and type of support will vary according to individual needs. Networks of people with mental health problems – 'user networks' – can provide essential support structures.[295] Evidence suggests however, that adults with severe mental health problems are five times, and those with common mental health problems are over twice as likely to report a perceived severe lack of support as those with no mental health problems.[296]

5. High levels of social support reduce the likelihood of a first occurrence of mental health problems,[297] and can increase quality of life for people with severe and enduring mental health problems.[298] In turn, low social support has been shown to reduce the likelihood of recovery.[299] Day services can be an effective means of providing support, as discussed in Chapter 4. There are a number of other ways of building social networks, some of which could also be accessed through day services.

- **Time banks**[300] provide opportunities for people to perform tasks for others, such as dog walking or giving lifts to the local shop. In return, they earn credits to spend on the services of other people. All members' time is valued equally. They are based on what people can offer rather than on what services they use. Research has linked participation in a time bank to a reduced reliance on GPs and an overall improvement in health.[301]

  "Rather than just keep going to your GP, you can always go to the community time bank people."

- **Circles of Friends** focus on supporting a person to build a strong social network to help them in achieving their goals. Some members of the circle are chosen for their personal skills or purely as friends, others for their professional ability or wider connections. A key role of members can be to act as a personal advocate, for example in assisting the person in their relationships with statutory bodies.

- **Faith and religious groups** can offer a powerful opportunity to build positive social networks for people with mental health problems. Rethink found that 40 per cent of adults with psychosis reported spirituality as a support.[302] Research has shown that aspects of spirituality are linked with beneficial mental health outcomes and are consistently related to greater life satisfaction, happiness, morale and other indicators of well-being.[303,304] This may be a particularly powerful link for some ethnic minority groups.[305] The Cares of Life project in Chapter 4 demonstrates that faith groups can be a safe and supportive setting in which to make the initial link to appropriate mental health services. Research with people with mental health problems found, however, that discussion of spirituality in mental health services was either ignored or seen as a sign of illness.[306]

Internet and telephone use

> *"Activities such as cinemas, parks, coffee shops ... are all important to people with mental health problems. Libraries are essential – I use the Internet there and it gives me somewhere to go during the day."*

6. People who do not have access to the Internet at home, such as those on low incomes, will often use libraries or other public places to go on-line.[307] People with mental health problems can also use the Internet in day services where they can receive extra support and assistance. One study found that nearly half of disabled people using the Internet felt that it had improved their quality of life compared to around a quarter of non-disabled people.[308] For people who may not be able to leave their homes, the Internet allows communication with others.[309] Research found that where services were accessible, 21 per cent of people with mental health problems identified the Internet as useful in overcoming isolation and 11 per cent identified the telephone.[310] There is a concern that when people are in hospital they can become very isolated from their social networks. This situation could be helped by access to email and Internet-based groups.

The voluntary and community sector

7. The voluntary and community sector is essential to deliver local services to adults with mental health problems and promote meaningful community engagement. Small local groups are better placed than government to understand and meet local community needs. This is particularly true of people who may be less likely to access statutory services, such as people from some ethnic minorities. However, short-term funding pressures can lead to effective programmes being closed or struggling to survive. The current spending review includes a review of how central and local government can better engage with the voluntary and community sector.

Black African and Caribbean Mental Health Consortium, Brent, London

The Consortium works with primary and secondary health care, the local authority, and local voluntary and community providers. It aims to build the trust of the Black African and Caribbean community to use health and social care services, and encourage integrated services for African-Caribbean mental health. The Consortium has established a monthly Ethnic Minority Mental Health Forum, and is the first local voluntary organisation to sign a compact with the local mental health trust. With the voluntary and community sector, it has developed a local database of groups offering services to ethnic minority communities and has analysed service gaps for the Black African and Caribbean community.

8. Increasing the community engagement of adults with mental health problems fits well with the government's **community cohesion** agenda, which is about proactive local action to promote greater knowledge, respect and contact between different cultures. The Community Cohesion Unit in the Home Office leads the government's strategy and works with a number of local authorities.

Family support

Parenting

"My consultant psychiatrist told my husband and I not to have children – 'they will be taken away, no doubt about it'. We now have a beautiful two and a half-year-old daughter; we are, to quote our GP, 'excellent parents'." [311]

9. A significant proportion of adults in contact with mental health services are **parents**.[312] Levels of depression are highest among the mothers of **young children**, **lone parents** and those who are **economically inactive**. 28 per cent of lone parents have common mental health problems.[313] Post-natal depression is estimated to affect one in ten new mothers and usually starts within six weeks of the birth.[314] Research suggests that a mother's prolonged post-natal depression may have a negative effect on the child's cognitive development and social relationships.[315]

10. Parental mental health problems can, but do not always, have a significant impact on children's social and emotional well-being by disrupting the attachment bond between infants and parents. A number of factors will determine how, and to what extent, parental mental health problems impact on a child's health and well-being. The severity of the diagnosis alone may not be a good guide because access to treatment, support, social and economic circumstances can have a significant impact on whether the child develops their own mental health problems.[316] Early recognition of mental health problems in parents, especially around birth, and provision of support can help prevent mental health problems from developing further. Providing early support to families can also help to prevent longer-term emotional and mental health problems among children.

"The worst part is when you're not sure how ill she is and if you should call the doctor or a friend. Sometimes she just sits and cries. My sister had to do lots of the housework when mum was ill. She felt that she was the mum, and mum was the child." [317]

11. An estimated one-third to two-thirds of children whose parents have mental health problems will experience difficulties themselves.[318] As noted in Chapter 3, parental mental health problems can lead to children being bullied at school because of the stigma surrounding mental health.[319]

12. Child care social workers estimate that 50-90 per cent of parents on their caseload either have mental health problems, alcohol or substance misuse issues.[320] One survey identified parental mental health problems as a key issue in 26 per cent of family support services' cases,[321] and it is a significant factor for children entering the care system.[322]

13. Many parents are able to carry out their parenting roles effectively, with appropriate support as necessary, yet a high proportion – 46 per cent of women and 28 per cent of men – feel that their parenting abilities have been unfairly questioned because of their mental health.[323] This can include people being advised not to have children.

14. A recent study of children caring for parents with mental health problems highlighted that parental hospitalisation can be a worrying and uncertain time for families, with parents and children fearing family separation due to loss of contact.[324] Very few children have contact with their parents when they are hospitalised, with parents often feeling the wards are not suitable places for children, making visiting sessions difficult. Families want better facilities to help them be together.

> *"I used to and still do hate going to see my mum in hospital, there is nowhere I can be alone with her. When I was little I used to be scared of going to see her because when we sat in the dining room the other patients used to come over and stroke my hair and hug me and kiss me and I didn't like this at all."* [325]

15. Research with parents found that they can have difficulty accessing mental health services to plan for their own and their families' needs before crises occur.[326] Mental health services do not always address the need for support with parenting, with parents with severe and enduring mental health problems rarely offered parenting and family support. Child protection assessments can focus more on assessing 'parental capacity' for child protection proceedings rather than providing support. Mental health services need to link effectively with children and families' services to provide a comprehensive service to meet families' needs.

Family Welfare Association, Building Bridges, Lewisham, London

In partnership with health and social services, the Building Bridges service provides support for families where a parent or carer is experiencing severe mental health problems and caring for a dependent child. It provides specialised support to bridge the gap between children's and adult mental health services. In 2002-03, nearly 80 per cent of clients were on income support, over 50 per cent were ethnic minorities and 70 per cent were lone parents. Services include:

- family-focused work to increase parenting skills, plan for periods of crisis, and provide home-based emotional and practical support and counselling for children;
- confidence-building group work for mothers, with a crèche for children; and
- training for local children's and community mental health team staff.

Deepna has severe depression, which necessitates stays in hospital. Her 13-year-old son used to miss school regularly to interpret for his mum at medical appointments; her seven-year-old daughter also often missed school due to anxiety. The Building Bridges project worked with another family member to accompany Deepna to medical appointments, and her son returned to school. Her daughter was helped to understand and talk about her mother's illness, and she returned to school. Deepna was able to attend parents' evening at school and go out on a trip with her. Without this intervention, her children would have been placed on the child protection register and may have been taken into care.

16. The government has invested heavily in recent years in improving support for parents, particularly parents of young children. **Sure Start** aims to provide co-ordinated and accessible services for pre-school children. Sure Start local programmes, children's centres and other early years services recognise the importance of parent-infant attachment for children's mental health and seek to promote and support positive bonding in a number of ways. For example, Sure Start in West Green and Chestnuts, Haringey, has developed multi-agency workshops and training on infant mental health, bringing together different professionals to talk about the stigma and discrimination surrounding mental health.

17. The Chancellor announced in the Budget 2003 that the government would examine the welfare reform and public service changes needed to advance faster towards its long-term goals to halve child poverty by 2010 and eradicate it by 2020. In the Budget 2004, the government announced additional funding for Sure Start including children's centres to provide services for all children in the 20 per cent most disadvantaged wards in England, and a total of 1700 centres by 2008, towards the goal of a children's centre in every community.

Carers

18. It can be difficult for carers to balance caring responsibilities with work and social activities. Carers are also twice as likely to have mental health problems themselves if they provide substantial care, which can impact on their ability to work.[327] The emotional impact can be equally strong, with family members seeing changes in the individual as a result of the illness, but not necessarily knowing how to help. When a family member has mental health problems, other members of the family are likely to take on additional caring responsibilities

> *"My own GP has no idea of the considerable emotional and practical input I have had into my son's everyday life for all these years. We fear what will happen when we are gone."* [328]

19. Research with carers found that support from social services is reduced when the person they care for is 'stable' rather than acutely unwell, and more than half felt they had no choice but to continue providing substantial support themselves. They are often concerned what will happen to their friend or relative in the future, for example, where elderly parents are caring for an adult son or daughter.[329]

20. In 1999, the Department of Health launched a **national strategy** for carers. In addition, the Mental Health National Service Framework and the NHS Plan outline requirements for mental health services to work with the family and wider community. The Department of Health produced *A Commitment to Carers* that informs families and friends what they should expect from mental health services. In January 2004, the Royal College of Psychiatrists and The Princess Royal Trust for Carers launched **Partners of Care**. This joint campaign will run for one year and concentrate on the problems faced by carers of all ages, of people with mental health problems and learning disabilities.

21. An estimated 6,000 to 17,000 **children and young people** care for an adult with mental health problems.[330] They often take on jobs and roles in the household when a parent or relative is unable to. Young carers say they want more information about the adult's health problems, greater recognition, and practical and domestic help, such as someone to talk to particularly in a crisis.[331] In Liverpool, the Barnardo's Action with Young Carers Project, *Keeping the Family in Mind*, has raised awareness of young carers' issues among health and social care professionals and contributed to the development of a family room within a local psychiatric unit.

Community roles

Volunteering

> *"To die seemed to be my only option; I had tried it on a few occasions. Then one of my key workers suggested that I applied to be a volunteer. It has changed my life. Even saved my life ... Volunteering gave me something to live for."*

22. In a recent survey, nine out of ten people with experience of using mental health services said that volunteering gave them a sense of purpose and achievement. More than eight out of ten also said that it had a positive effect on their mental health, and four out of ten said it had increased their chances of employment.[332]

23. People can access volunteering opportunities through local councils for voluntary services, local volunteer bureaux, or national initiatives such as TimeBank[333], a web-based national campaign to raise the profile of volunteering and increase opportunities and participation.

24. The Active Communities Unit in the Home Office is responsible for developing new initiatives to encourage diversity in community participation and explore barriers to volunteering for specific groups. Other national initiatives providing advice and guidance on volunteering include *You Cannot be Serious*, a comprehensive guide to involving volunteers with mental health problems, produced by the Department of Health and the National Centre for Volunteering.[334]

> *"I went to help out at the local charity shop for one afternoon a week ... After the first week they wanted me to work four days a week, I tried to do it as I didn't want to make a fuss, but on the third day I became so stressed I had to leave the shop. I'm not volunteering again, I couldn't cope with it."*

25. Appropriate support is crucial to ensure that enthusiasm for volunteering is not damaged by negative experiences or unrealistic expectations. There has been an increase in supported volunteering, whereby individuals are offered help to find a volunteering placement, and are supported once in post.[335]

> *"We always say to volunteers that they should let Jobcentre Plus know what they are doing. But you can see how afraid they are to make contact. They're worried that taking up a few hours volunteering will affect their benefits."*

26. Despite the recent abolition of the benefit rule setting out that individuals claiming Incapacity Benefit could only volunteer for 16 hours or less a week, there is still some confusion over the existing rules and a persisting fear that volunteering might jeopardise entitlement to benefit.

Volunteering and Benefits

Incapacity Benefit
Incapacity Benefit claimants are allowed to do an unlimited amount of voluntary work. Benefit issues might arise when payment is involved or if the activity appears incompatible with the benefits claim – for example, if someone claiming IB because of back pain took a voluntary position that involved heavy lifting.

Jobseekers' Allowance
There are no restrictions on the amount of voluntary activity that can be undertaken by Jobseekers' Allowance claimants as long as they continue to satisfy the conditions of entitlement. Volunteers can now give seven days notice (instead of 48 hours) to rearrange or give up a volunteer position in order to take up paid employment. Claimants are still required to be available for an interview at 48 hours' notice.

Taking on civic responsibility

> *"One of our members is trusted by her employer with a budget of £30 million and clinical responsibility for services to 8,000 people. Yet she is not permitted to serve on a jury."* [336]

27. Current legislation disqualifies anyone from serving as a **member of a jury** if they have experienced a mental health problem that has led to a hospital admission or regular attendance for treatment by a medical practitioner.[337] There is no publicly available guidance on how to interpret this disqualification but potentially the criteria could be applied very widely, such as covering people with minor depression prescribed medication by their GP.

28. People summoned for jury service are required to declare whether they suffer from one of the mental disorders listed on the jury summoning form. Completion of this part of the form results in automatic disqualification – around 8 per cent of all disqualifications are on mental health grounds.

In 1999, the Disability Rights Taskforce recommended that the definition should be considered further.[338] Lord Justice Auld's report, *Review of the Criminal Courts* (2001), recommended the removal of certain jury exemption categories but did not propose any change to the mental health ineligibility criteria.[339]

29. At any one time, there are around 42,000 vacancies for **school governors**.[340] The Department for Education and Skills encourages the widest possible range of people to apply to become governors through initiatives such as GovernorNet and the Governors' One Stop Shop.[341]

30. The Department for Education and Skills updated the regulations on school governors with effect from April 2004, to clarify that people '*liable* to be detained' under the Mental Health Act 1983 are no longer barred from being school governors.[342] The previous wording had caused confusion, and increased the risk that potential governors who had spent time in hospital in the past or might need to do so in the future may have been deterred from applying. The new regulations now state that *"A person is disqualified from holding or continuing to hold office as a governor of a school at any time when he is detained under the Mental Health Act 1983."*

Accessing services in the community

31. Using community services can improve confidence and self-esteem, provide opportunities to meet new people, and help strengthen existing relationships with family and friends. Local services, such as colleges or arts and sports activities, can offer opportunities to meet people from outside mental health services and integrate into the local community.

32. Some projects are run solely for people with mental health problems (usually severe and enduring mental health problems), with fewer opportunities for wider community integration. Alternatively, people might use mainstream community provision, such as the local further education college, perhaps with additional support from mental health services or a voluntary provider. In some cases, a project might be run by mental health services but be open to anyone from the local community – such as a café providing work experience to people with mental health problems which is open to the public.

Education and training

Wigan and Leigh Further Education College

The Inclusive Learning Team at Wigan and Leigh College provides individual assessment and additional support to any learner with a mental health problem or other learning difficulty. Most students follow nationally accredited programmes, with provision from entry level through to higher education, in a number of vocational areas. Mentoring is available for students with mental health problems. Team members work closely with the local NHS trust partnership and local social service teams. Staff training is provided on an ongoing basis. Over 200 students are currently accessing college programmes under this service, with funding provided by the Learning and Skills Council.

"I'd love to go back to education. I'm in my 50s now, but they've said I'm bright and that I could go back to college – get some more education. But no one's pushed me towards it."

"If I hadn't come to university, I'm sure I'd be dead by now."

33. One-third of respondents to the Social Exclusion Unit's consultation identified access to education and training opportunities as a key issue. Participation in learning can have a positive effect on mental health.[343] Benefits can include:

- acquiring new skills;
- feeling more empowered and having a greater sense of purpose;
- being viewed more positively by others;
- establishing new friendships; and
- access to better jobs, better housing and easier access to leisure pursuits.

34. People with low levels of educational achievement are likely to have less income and be less healthy overall.[344] A lack of qualifications can cause and reinforce social exclusion for people with mental health problems. Among people with common mental health problems, just under one in three have no qualifications, and one-third have qualifications at GCSE level equivalent.[345]

35. Ethnic minority groups may be less able to access learning than other groups with mental health problems. This may be because of low expectations within specialist mental health services, or because of language barriers if learners lack confidence in speaking English and provision of language courses is inflexible.[346]

36. Moving into learning can be a big step for people with mental health problems. The type of learning support available can play a crucial role in helping people choose where to study and whether to continue learning. Most colleges encourage mainstream learning as it allows greater integration into college life and increases understanding of mental health problems among other students.

Barnet College and College of North East London

Barnet, Enfield and Haringey Mental Health Trust and the local education authority fund the College Link Programme at Barnet College and the College of NE London. The programme offers specially designed courses for people with mental health problems, with a limited number of Sure Start funded childcare places. Students are supported on site by an assistant psychologist link worker. An audit of the programme analysed its impact on health service costs, including hospital services, and found an overall saving of £8,000 per student. After completing the programme almost all students moved into mainstream education or some form of employment.

Forms of learning

There are three main types of learning provision for adults:

- **Adult and Community Learning (ACL)** is based in the community and often targets the needs of specific groups of learners. ACL allows learning to be more flexible and less formal.
- **Further Education (FE)** is for people over compulsory school age (16 in England). It can take place in a school sixth-form, a sixth-form college, a further education college or a higher education institution.
- **Higher Education (HE)** courses include degree courses, foundation degrees, postgraduate courses and Higher National Diplomas. Learning takes place in universities, HE colleges and in some FE colleges.

37. Some further education colleges have well-established support mechanisms delivered through specialist teams. For example, New College Nottingham has close links with local health services and a programme that includes outreach, specialist and mainstream provision. Almost all higher education institutions have pastoral and counselling services, and there are many examples of good practice in identifying and supporting students with mental health problems.[347] Guidance has been produced by the higher education sector on student mental health policies and procedures, reducing student suicide, and a good practice guide for student services.[348] In 2003, a group of HE bodies, agencies and professional groups with responsibility for student mental health formed an influential committee to promote collaboration across the sector.[349]

Nottingham Trent University

The Progression Support Team at Nottingham Trent University focuses on the practical difficulties faced by students with established mental health problems, and those who may be vulnerable to developing them. The support is marketed variously as assisting students to overcome barriers that they face to academic progression and providing specialist support to students with mental health problems. This allows a non-stigmatising access route to services, but also offers assurance of a quality service to those who are open about their mental health problems.

The service assists students to increase understanding of the impact of their health and lifestyle on their education (and vice versa), and enables them to develop appropriate coping strategies. It also liaises over changes to methods of academic assessment and tutorial support. This involves the whole institution in mental health promotion, and ensures compliance with the Disability Discrimination Act. In a typical academic year, the team supports approximately 200 students, of whom around 35 will receive funding through the Disabled Student Allowance.

38. Adult and community learning can be accessed through voluntary sector projects or local community and outreach services. Some mental health trusts have set up their own learning and support services for students. Each service varies in its level of partnership working with local education providers, with differing degrees of emphasis placed on the therapeutic nature of the work or on social inclusion.

39. The National Institute for Mental Health in England is working with the National Institute of Adult Continuing Education to improve access to mainstream adult education. Their research found that growing numbers of colleges and Local Education Authorities (LEAs) have developed learning provision for people with mental health problems in recent years. 60 per cent of colleges and 68 per cent of LEAs reported that they were actively recruiting learners with mental health problems.[350]

40. Under the Disability Discrimination Act, all providers of post-school education have a legal duty not to discriminate against disabled students, either by treating them less favourably for a reason related to their disability or failing to make reasonable adjustments. The new legislation came into force in September 2002. By September 2005, all institutions will have to ensure that their physical facilities meet the need of disabled students.

41. Comprehensive and reliable data on the number of students with mental health problems in further and higher education is not available, and no figures exist on participation in adult and community learning. Published statistics on students with disabilities suggest low participation rates, with around a quarter of 1 per cent of students declaring a disability for mental health reasons.[351] However, this is likely to be an underestimate because it is based on self-reporting. Many students do not disclose mental health problems, either because they do not consider their condition to be a disability, for fear of stigma, or they do not believe the college needs to know. However, recent research found that half way through their studies, 9 per cent of students had become depressed and 20 per cent had become anxious at a clinical level.[352]

42. Chapter 8 describes the barriers that people with mental health problems face when trying to access services, such as a lack of support, or transport. In addition, barriers to accessing education include:

- low expectations, with colleges and health and social workers assuming that potential learners cannot or do not want to access mainstream education and will not want to undertake accredited courses;
- inflexible courses that do not take account of fluctuating health;
- complicated enrolment procedures;
- low confidence, or earlier negative experiences at school; and
- financial concerns, such as tuition fees, transport, and text books.

43. Disabled Students' Allowances provide financial assistance for disabled students in higher education to cover the extra disability-related costs in attending the course. Only a very small proportion of students with mental health-related disabilities are currently awarded DSAs, with significant variations between higher education institutions (between 0 and 14 per cent).[353] This may be for a number of reasons:

- the invisibility of the health problem;
- mental health problems not being seen as disabilities;
- the perceived formality and lack of transparency of application procedures discouraging potential applicants; or
- the lack of standardisation of awards procedures across regions.

Arts, leisure and sports

44. Over one-third of respondents to the Social Exclusion Unit consultation highlighted access to recreational activities as essential to promote social inclusion. Three-quarters of adults with common mental health problems say they would have liked *more* leisure activity over the last year, compared with just over half of those with no mental health problems.[354]

45. Studies have shown that people respond well to GP advice to take more **exercise**.[355] The positive effects of physical exercise include:

- increased well-being and reduced anxiety and depression;[356]
- improved physical health including losing weight; and
- acting as a distraction from hearing voices.

Swan Leisure Centre, Berwick upon Tweed

Swan Leisure Centre runs a 12-week programme for people with mental health problems. The programme is an exercise referral programme with people referred by GPs, physiotherapists, occupational therapists or social services. Individuals must have medical clearance from their GP prior to taking part and pay an initial fee of £8. Then, people may attend up to three sessions per week from Monday to Friday at concessionary rates. Following the first 12-week period participants may renew on the referral scheme if they wish. Carers may use the facility for free if accompanying somebody on the scheme.

Additionally, two mental health gym groups are run once a week, which offers people the opportunity to meet others in a social environment and take part in closely supervised activity.

46. **Arts** are believed to have a therapeutic role as well as helping people reintegrate into wider society by increasing self-esteem, confidence and social networks. In one survey, roughly half of participants reported feeling better or healthier since becoming involved in the arts.[357] Another showed that when people worked with artists on discharge from hospital there were fewer re-admissions.[358] However, systematic reviews of the social, clinical and cost benefits of participation in arts in mental health programmes are needed.

> *"I didn't expect this at 70 years of age. It has done more for me than the medication and also made a childhood dream come true – to do art."*

47. Participation in arts and creative activities is often facilitated through mental health day centres and other health settings, such as the arts on prescription projects described in Chapter 4. They are also accessed through local voluntary and community sector projects. Less is done to support people taking up activities in mainstream settings.

Start, Manchester

Start is based within Manchester Mental Health & Social Care Trust, and provides art and activity studios, a gallery and a café. It offers educational opportunities and career paths in visual arts and design to over 100 people with severe and enduring mental health needs. The top 10 per cent of students are being encouraged to set up a co-operative studio business in art and design, 5 per cent are undertaking supported teacher training and workshop technician placements in community venues, and a further 20 per cent are being supported into mainstream education by means of special bridging courses.

Conclusions

Mental health problems can have a significant impact on families. Early, non-stigmatising family support, and better links between adult mental health services and children and family services can improve parents' mental health and prevent children's or carers' mental health problems from developing.

Strong social networks can promote a sense of well-being, help develop confidence, and allow greater access to employment, education or volunteering opportunities. Too many people with mental health problems have limited contact with people from outside mental health services. People can engage with the local community through being a volunteer or by accessing mainstream services such as college or leisure activities.

Action taken as a result of this report will improve the support available to parents with mental health problems, and promote access to education, volunteering and arts opportunities.

CHAPTER 8: Getting the basics right

Summary

- People with mental health problems frequently have housing problems, such as rent arrears or poorly maintained accommodation. Most live in mainstream housing and around half live alone.
- Many experience high levels of debt. They can lack advice on financial and legal issues, and be denied access to financial services.
- One in four people experience difficulties accessing mental health services through an inability to pay for transport.
- People can also need information and advice to enable them to find employment or participate in local communities.

1. People with mental health problems may not be able to access activities such as employment or volunteering unless basic issues are addressed.

- Decent and stable *housing* is critical to providing a sense of security.
- People need access to basic *financial* and *transport* services.
- People need practical *information and advice* about opportunities in the community. Some need additional *support* to take up these opportunities.

Housing

"No one seems to consider the link between mental health problems and housing problems ... Social landlords should be far more pro-active in identifying tenants who may need additional help."

2. Stable, appropriate housing is critical for people to work and take part in community life. A lack of stability or unsatisfactory housing can lead to worsening mental health. People with mental health problems are particularly likely to have vulnerable housing. Compared with the general population, they are:

- **one and a half times** more likely to live in rented housing, with higher uncertainty about how long they can remain in their current home;
- **twice** as likely to say that they are very dissatisfied with their accommodation or that the state of repair is poor; and
- **four times** more likely to say that their health has been made worse by their housing.[359]

Social housing

> **Look Ahead Housing & Care, Tower Hamlets, London**
>
> Look Ahead is a registered social landlord that provides support and care to vulnerable people including those at risk of losing their housing due to mental health problems. The Tower Hamlets project has a multi-disciplinary team that concentrates on early intervention and working closely with tenants and a range of professionals to provide an intensive mental health outreach care service to people living in their homes.
>
> The team focuses on practical issues, such as ensuring that rent and bills are paid, as well as a range of other practical, social and life skills. The service makes it possible for people with enduring mental health problems to remain in their homes by effectively linking them up with a strong local social support network.

3. One in four tenants with mental health problems has serious rent arrears and risks losing their home.[360] Rent arrears are behind 90 per cent of possession cases. The threat of eviction can have a pronounced negative effect on mental health, as well as each eviction costing between £2,000-£3,000 for the local authority or registered social landlord.

4. Following the closure of long-stay psychiatric hospitals, there has been a move to more diverse housing. Housing providers include local housing authorities, housing associations, voluntary organisations and health services. Over four out of five people with severe and enduring mental health problems live in mainstream housing, with the rest living in supported housing or other specialist accommodation. Half of those with their own home or tenancy live alone.[361]

5. Under current homelessness legislation, people with mental health problems who are homeless may be considered to have a 'priority need' for accommodation by the local housing authority. Around nine per cent of applicants accepted by local housing authorities in England as being owed a main homelessness duty are considered to have a priority need for accommodation because they are vulnerable as a result of mental health problems.

Figure 13: Households in priority housing need – mental illness, England 1997 to 2003

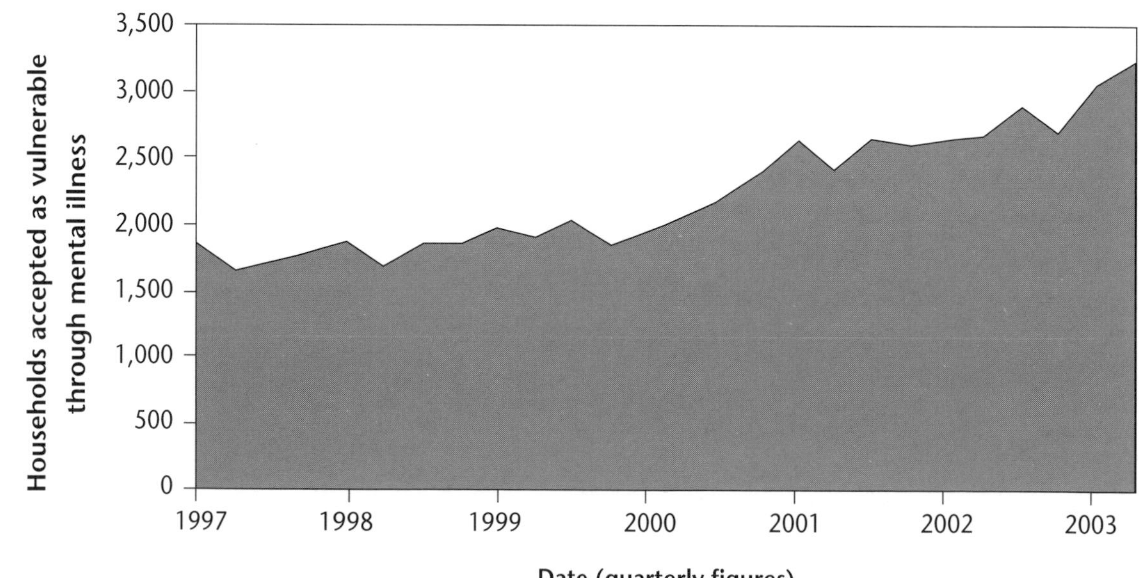

Source: Office of the Deputy Prime Minister, Quarterly Statistics.

6. There is often a significant gap between being accepted as in 'priority need' under the homelessness legislation and finding settled accommodation, during which people will be housed temporarily, sometimes in bed and breakfast accommodation. This can be particularly problematic for people who need stability. The use of bed and breakfast accommodation fell by a third last year, but the overall number of people in temporary accommodation rose by 13 per cent.[362] The Office of the Deputy Prime Minister recently amended the homelessness legislation so that local housing authorities can no longer discharge a homelessness duty in respect of families with dependent children, or households including a pregnant woman, by placing them in bed and breakfast accommodation for more than six weeks.

7. Some sectors of the population have higher rates of homelessness, although data can be unreliable. Among those who are heads of households, people from black and ethnic minority communities are estimated to be three times more likely to have experienced homelessness than white people. Members of ethnic minority groups are less likely to be homeless on the street, and are more likely to stay with friends and relatives – a form of 'hidden homelessness'. They make up 22 per cent of households accepted as homeless.[363]

8. People with mental health problems might stay in homeless hostels or acute psychiatric wards because there is no suitable move-on accommodation. Some studies have estimated that around a quarter of people in supported housing or residential care want to move.[364] Stays of five years or longer in temporary housing in London are now common.

> *"I'd say that there were about six people out of the 20 on our rehabilitation ward who have been ready to move on to other accommodation for some time. Having them still on the ward is a waste."*

9. Many housing authorities operate a 'one offer' policy for people on housing waiting lists, with a very short period in which to accept an offer or return to the back of the queue. Accommodation offered at short notice can be unfurnished. Such immediate decisions can place clients with mental health problems under considerable strain. Appeals often rely on having good advice or advocacy workers, but these may not always be accessible. The government has been piloting a new approach to letting social housing ("Choice Based Lettings"), which offers social housing tenants a greater say in where they live. All housing authorities are expected to have implemented Choice Based Lettings approaches by 2010.

Assessment and Resettlement Team, Bromley, London

The Assessment and Resettlement Team in the local housing department is responsible for everyone over the age of 16 who is deemed 'vulnerable', including those with mental health problems. The team links health, social care and housing services to ensure that people who are re-housed have the best opportunity to maintain their tenancy. Part of their role is to vet potential properties to ensure that they are suitable and go with clients to the viewing. All team members specialising in mental health have previously worked in a community mental health team. In the last year the team has worked with over 400 people.

10. Anecdotal evidence from housing and health workers suggests that 'residential sorting' can take place, with people with mental health problems ending up in the same few local neighbourhoods and estates, placing pressure on local services and isolating communities.

11. The National Service Framework for Mental Health states that local partners in health and social care should develop plans for vulnerable groups, including homeless people.

Supporting People

Supporting People came into operation in 2003. It facilitates independent living through housing-related support services for vulnerable people aged 16 and over. It is delivered on the ground by local authorities through working partnerships with the health and probation services, service providers and users. Supporting People links housing support with the care and mental health services funded under the Care Programme Approach. Access routes to Supporting People programmes include health and social services, GPs, housing departments and self-referral.

The government intends to issue guidance on accommodation and support options for people with mental health problems later this year. Support needs include:

- preventing mental health problems from escalating through early access to appropriate services;
- resolving housing-related crises for those at risk of homelessness through eviction or abandonment of a tenancy; and
- resettlement and rehabilitation in stable housing following homelessness or time in unstable accommodation.

Owner occupation

12. In comparison with work on mental health and social housing, there is little research on existing or potential owner occupiers. Most research has been related to debt, with one study finding that up to four out of five people with mortgage arrears were suffering from depression.[365]

13. There is little data on people's experiences in obtaining mortgages, but research suggests particular difficulties obtaining life insurance, increasingly crucial to getting a mortgage.[366] The increased risk of having a low income and an unstable employment history will also be barriers to owner occupation for people with mental health problems. Options such as 'shared ownership' are an important way of moving towards owner-occupation for people unable or unwilling to take on significant mortgage commitments. Tenants buy between 25 per cent and 75 per cent of the property, paying a subsidised rent on the remaining share.

Financial and legal issues

"My illness, depression and stress has been exacerbated by my debt problem. As a result I cannot get well enough to go back to work to earn money to pay the debts." [367]

14. Financial problems are the most frequently cited cause of depression, but can also be a consequence of mental health problems.[368] People with mental health problems are nearly three times as likely to be in debt, and more than twice as likely to have problems managing money as the general population.[369] Lacking a bank account is associated with depression, and people who have to borrow money from agencies or individuals other than banks or building societies have poorer mental health than those who have better access to credit.[370]

15. Research around access to financial services makes few specific links to mental health. Financial exclusion is concentrated in the most deprived areas of the country, with twice as many people likely to be financially excluded as those in similar circumstances in less deprived areas.[371] People who are long-term unemployed or claiming benefits are particularly likely to be financially excluded.[372] These are all groups where there is significant over-representation of people with mental health problems.

16. By 2005, most people will have their benefits paid into either an existing bank account, a Post Office Card Account, or one of the new Basic Bank Accounts offered by all major banks and building societies. These allow for basic banking, but do not provide cheque or overdraft facilities. Recent research has suggested that there can be difficulties accessing Basic Bank Accounts, with problems around personal identification or people being offered more sophisticated accounts than needed.[373] These are particularly significant issues for people with mental health problems.

17. Research published this year has shown the extent to which some people with mental health problems experience difficulties as consumers of everyday goods and services. Pressured sales techniques and discrimination due to a lack of knowledge of the symptoms of mental illness can be particular problems.[374]

Disability Living Allowance

Disability Living Allowance (DLA) contributes towards the additional care and mobility costs associated with having a disability. It can be paid whether someone is in or out of work, if they live on their own or with a carer, and is not related to income. To be eligible, people must have demonstrated the prescribed amount of care needs for three months because of severe mental or physical disabilities, and be likely to have those care needs for at least a further six months. Of those currently receiving DLA, 14 per cent receive it because of mental health problems.[375]

Decisions on entitlement to DLA are made by non-medical staff in the Disability and Carer Service, part of the Department for Work and Pensions. Decisions are based on the claimant's self-assessment of their disability, together with any additional evidence that the decision maker considers to be necessary. This may include, for example, factual reports from GPs, hospital doctors and health care professionals. There is a high rate of successful appeals for DLA.

18. Many people with mental health problems claiming Disability Living Allowance have concerns that if they returned to work, or took steps towards finding work, they would be judged no longer to have the additional care needs provided for by DLA as they would be deemed 'better'. The return to work is often a stressful time, with many people needing more support (including that provided for by DLA), not less. A further complication is that people receiving Income Support as well as DLA often receive a single payment from Jobcentre Plus, so when Income Support payments stop, this can disrupt DLA payments.

Financial and legal advice

"We rarely ever get to see people at the right time – perhaps two or three per cent come in then. With the rest it's always at the last minute – usually with the eviction notice or a warrant in their hand."

19. Recent research into how people deal with serious problems found that people with mental health problems were least likely to take specific action to resolve the problem. Over six out of ten people said this was because they thought nothing could be done. Those who did take action often did so alone, with nearly eight out of ten people not seeking advice first.[376]

20. Many people seeking financial or legal advice will use local voluntary organisations. This can put a real strain on local resources. Over **one in six** Citizens Advice Bureau clients are currently suffering from one or more common mental health problem.[377] In some areas, such as Salford and

Northumberland, the CAB and local healthcare providers have responded by introducing specialist advice in day centres and hospitals. However, such schemes are often subject to short-term funding problems.

21. Local advocacy services, independent organisations usually funded by health and social care agencies, provide active support in assisting clients to resolve practical difficulties such as around benefits and housing. Community Legal Service Partnerships assess gaps or overlaps in local provision, and identify areas of specific need. They provide information and analysis to local funding bodies, such as the Legal Services Commission or local authorities. A key task is to ensure effective referral systems for all those who may require assistance.

Independent Advocacy Service, Cambridgeshire

The advocacy service provides people with mental health problems across Cambridgeshire with help to access information and support. The service is jointly funded by the local primary care trust and city council, and is free, independent and confidential. The advocate is there to ensure that clients have an opportunity to speak up for themselves and get their voice heard. Working at the client's direction, the advocate can support the client to deal with issues including housing, financial services, welfare benefits, and legal issues, as well as practical help with forms and letters. All advocates are able to point to the practical results of their work, for example, one has helped five of his clients prevent their eviction. As one client said, *"Advocacy has enabled me to review the circumstances of my life and find a practical way forward."*

Insurance

"I have a well-paid job with lots of security, but because I sometimes go into hospital with a mental health problem I can't find travel insurance that I can afford."

22. In one study, a quarter of people with mental health problems said that they had been refused insurance or other financial services.[378] In response to long-standing concerns, the Association of British Insurers produced guidance in 2003 that set out insurers' responsibilities to people covered by the Disability Discrimination Act 1995.[379] Insurers should offer the same cover and terms wherever possible, unless there are lawful reasons based on relevant and reliable data. The Association also recognises that best practice principles within the guide are widely applicable to all people with mental health problems. There is a standing commitment to re-issue the guide as new issues come to light. Where individual problems arise, the Financial Ombudsman Service can consider complaints relating to insurance decisions. This service is free.

23. Despite these advances, ongoing concerns include:

- the degree to which insurance companies' risk and outcome information is based on the real experiences of people with mental health problems;
- the skills and knowledge of front-line staff in dealing with applications from people with a mental health problem; and
- the extent to which people's perceptions of discrimination affect their willingness to disclose information about their mental health, potentially invalidating their claims.

24. In response to these difficulties, a small number of organisations have begun to develop specialist provision, for example the Manic Depression Fellowship has negotiated affordable life and travel insurance premiums for its members.

Loonscape.com

Loonscape.com aims to improve access to financial services and business opportunities for people using mental health services. It was created to support employed people to access basic financial services. Loonscape.com is working alongside other organisations to act as a gateway to a range of financial products and services specifically tailored to this group.

Access to justice

> *"My human rights are something I fight daily to have recognised. When I sought an injunction against a man who had been violent to me for 15 years, I was subject to psychiatric reports to establish my credibility as a witness."*

25. People who use mental health services can encounter difficulties in accessing the same legal protection as other members of the community. They may be seen as unreliable witnesses or as unable to cope with the pressure of legal proceedings. This can result in legitimate cases not being pursued and, in the worst cases, a local culture where people with mental health problems are seen as beneath the law.

26. The Youth Justice and Criminal Evidence Act (1999) introduced support systems for vulnerable witnesses, including people with mental health problems. Vulnerable witnesses may now be eligible to give video recorded evidence, give evidence over a live TV link, or have screens around the witness box. The Act also reformed the law on competence, so that the presumption is that all witnesses are competent to testify, with support as needed, unless they cannot understand the questions asked of them. Guidance issued in 2002 includes specific sections on supporting witnesses with mental health problems.[380] The new provisions are currently being evaluated.

27. There are a number of ways in which local schemes can build on such national initiatives. Schemes such as the Patient Advisory Liaison Service (PALS) and the advocacy services provide a valuable way of ensuring that complaints are taken seriously and are fully investigated.

28. Statistics regularly show that people from some ethnic minority communities are over-represented in their contact with the criminal justice system. Black people are eight times more likely to be stopped and searched than white people, and five times more likely to be arrested than any other ethnic group.[381]

29. The reasons behind this over-representation are complex. Around 48 per cent of the ethnic minority population is under 24 years of age (the peak age for offending), compared to 31 per cent of the white population.[382] People from some ethnic minority backgrounds are also disproportionately likely to suffer from other aspects of social exclusion, particularly unemployment, poor skills and living in deprived areas. In turn these issues have a link to mental health problems.

30. The *Mental Incapacity Bill* is due for publication shortly. It will lay out a single test of incapacity to be assessed according to each decision which needs to be taken, thus allowing for fluctuating capacity. Provisions to allow people to create a Lasting Power of Attorney, who may be a friend, link-worker or family member, may help when people with mental health problems are admitted to hospital, because they will enable financial and benefits issues to be dealt with while the person is in hospital.

Transport

"Even where there is no current problem in claiming in the city there are constant problems on buses of driver prejudice e.g. 'Why have you got a pass, you don't look ill'." [383]

31. Access to many activities to promote social inclusion, such as employment, education or arts and sports activities, relies on available transport, and the appropriate location, design and delivery of those services.[384] In rural areas, there are particularly acute difficulties around access to essential services, because services are further apart and involve greater distances, and because of the reduced frequency of public transport.

32. Research suggests that up to one in four people have been unable to get help from mental health services due to an inability to pay for transport.[385] A small number of people with mental health problems are automatically eligible for reduced cost travel via schemes such as concessionary fares on buses – for example, those who would be unable to get a driving licence because of severe mental health problems.[386] Local authorities have the discretion to offer concessionary fares more widely than the statutory minimum, although transport providers are not obliged to participate in such discretionary schemes. There is evidence that many people are unaware of local entitlements where these exist,[387] and eligibility tends to be more restricted than for people with physical disabilities.

33. Despite the widespread prevalence of mental health problems and the importance of appropriate transport in helping people to access work and other activities, mental health rarely features within local transport planning systems.

Information and advice

34. As seen in Chapter 4, health and social care services can play a crucial role in providing information about and referrals to local services. Local voluntary and community groups can also be important sources of help, for example local **Citizens Advice Bureaux** and organisations such as **Councils for Voluntary Service**. These can be particularly important for people who may be less likely to engage with statutory services, such as people from some ethnic minority groups or homeless people.

35. Young people aged 13 to 19 can receive information, advice and support from **Connexions Personal Advisers**, some of whom will have an understanding of common mental health problems. Where a personal adviser does not have the specialist knowledge to meet a young person's needs, they will be able to broker specialist services for the young person, but they receive little formal training in disability equality or about disability-related programmes or services. People with learning difficulties or disabilities can receive assistance until their 25th birthday where necessary. Mental health problems are one of the areas covered by *Connexions Direct*, an advice line and website that provides information and contact details for further advice.

36. The Department for Education and Skills is currently reviewing the work of the **Information, Advice and Guidance** service to ensure that all adults will have access to information on disability and employment issues by August 2004. This advice will also act as a gateway to more specialist support.

37. Other national initiatives include **Worktrain**, run by the Department for Work and Pensions, which provides real-time, on-line information about training, employment and childcare opportunities. **LearnDirect**, available via the Internet or telephone, offers information about training and education opportunities. However, it can sometimes be difficult for people with mental health problems to access IT or telephone-based sources of advice, and services based on outreach can be more effective.

38. A significant number of voluntary organisations provide information and advice specifically for people with mental health problems via telephone helplines or the Internet. These include Mind's Mind*infoLine*, the Mental Health Foundation website and the National Advice Service run by Rethink. The **Mental Health Helplines Partnership** is in the process of developing across the board guidance and standards in this area.

Conclusions

Stable housing, help with finances, and access to transport are crucial, both to promote positive mental health, and to enable people to find jobs or take up other opportunities in the community. People also need information about the different options available, and some will need additional support to access these opportunities. Chapter 9 of this report identifies action to prevent housing evictions and improve access to financial advice and affordable transport.

Chapter 9: The government's action plan

1. This report has set out why further action is needed to tackle the social exclusion still experienced by too many people with mental health problems. Our vision is of a future where people with mental health problems have the same opportunities to work and participate in their communities as any other citizen. This will mean:

- communities accepting that people with mental health problems are equal;
- people receiving the support they need *before* they reach crisis point;
- people having genuine choices and a real say about what they do and the support they receive in order to fulfil their potential;
- people keeping jobs longer, returning to employment faster and with real opportunities for career progression;
- recognition of the fundamental importance of people's relationships, family and caring responsibilities, a decent home and participation in social and leisure activities; and
- health and social care services working in close partnership with employment and community services, with fair access regardless of ethnicity, gender, age or sexuality.

2. The action plan set out in this chapter will contribute to the delivery of a number of departmental **Public Service Agreement targets**, in particular:

- the Department for Work and Pensions' target to **increase the employment rate of people with disabilities**, taking account of the economic cycle, and significantly reduce the difference between their employment rate and the overall rate, and to work to **improve the rights of disabled people and remove barriers to their participation in society**;
- the Department of Health target to **improve life outcomes of adults and children with mental health problems** through year on year improvements in access to crisis and Child and Adult Mental Health services, and **reduce the mortality rate from suicide and undetermined injury** by at least 20 per cent by 2010;
- the Department of Health target to **reduce inequalities in health outcomes** by 10 per cent by 2010 as measured by infant mortality and life expectancy at birth; and
- the joint Department for Work and Pensions and HM Treasury target to reduce the number of children in low-income households by at least a quarter by 2004, as a contribution towards the broader target of **halving child poverty by 2010 and eradicating it by 2020**.

3. This chapter sets out a 27-point action plan bringing together the work of government departments and other organisations in a concerted effort to challenge attitudes and significantly improve opportunities and outcomes for this excluded group. Action falls into six categories:

- **stigma and discrimination** – a sustained programme to challenge negative attitudes and promote awareness of people's rights;

- **the role of health and social care in tackling social exclusion** – implementing evidence-based practice in vocational services and enabling reintegration into the community;
- **employment** – giving people with mental health problems a real chance of sustained paid work based on their experience and skills;
- **supporting families and community participation** – enabling people to lead fulfilling lives the way they choose;
- **getting the basics right** – access to decent homes, financial advice and transport; and
- **making it happen** – clear arrangements for leading this programme and maintaining momentum.

4. There are strong links between these different sections, and they cannot be viewed in isolation. Tackling stigma and discrimination is a priority for all organisations and services across sectors. The advice and treatment people receive from health and social care services is critical in enabling people to fulfil their aspirations and make the most of opportunities in the community – whether work or other activities. Strengthening social networks can open up opportunities for employment, while being in work can widen opportunities for social interactions. Access to basic services – in particular decent housing and transport – is fundamental in enabling people to take up these opportunities.

5. The action plan is for England only. However, where actions relate to retained matters, such as employment and benefits policy, they apply to all devolved administrations. The Social Exclusion Unit project has drawn lessons from Wales, Scotland and Northern Ireland and the report is likely to be relevant throughout the UK.

Stigma and discrimination

6. The Social Exclusion Unit's consultation highlighted that stigma and discrimination is the greatest single barrier to achieving better integration into the community for people with mental health problems. People who disclose their condition are too often rejected or excluded as a result; while those who are too ashamed or fearful to disclose can fail to get the support they need until they reach crisis point.

7. Much progress has been made in recent decades in tackling discrimination on grounds of race, gender and sexuality, but stereotypes about 'madness' remain culturally acceptable. International evidence indicates that sustained work to target discriminatory behaviour is the best way to achieve behavioural change.

8. Challenging stigma and discrimination is an underpinning theme throughout all the actions within this plan which span a wide range of organisations and sectors. This is not a problem that can be solved simply through an awareness-raising campaign. The more adults with mental health problems are enabled to participate within mainstream activities and disclose their condition, the easier it will be to overcome unhelpful stereotypes. The public sector, individuals, employers, service providers and the wider community all have a responsibility and role in tackling stigma and discrimination.

<table>
<tr><th>Action</th><th>Detail</th><th>Who and when</th></tr>
<tr><td>1) Challenge stigma and discrimination</td><td>A strengthened and sustained programme of work to challenge stigma and discrimination will be led by the National Institute for Mental Health in England (NIMHE) working closely with other government departments, people with experience of mental health problems, carers and the voluntary sector through a board of advisers. The programme is backed by £1.1 million investment in 2004-05 and will:
• be based on international evidence of what works, and learn from previous mental health and health promotion campaigns;
• target key audiences, in particular employers, young people and the media;
• deliver consistent, tested messages under a single brand;
• promote the positive contribution that people with mental health problems can make to society;
• have sustained funding to plan ahead;
• address issues of ethnicity and gender;
• provide a framework and materials to support local campaign work, targeting in particular issues facing deprived neighbourhoods;
• be clearly evaluated by a regular survey.

NIMHE will also monitor trends reported by Ofcom in mental health portrayal by the broadcast media, and make recommendations to Ofcom on the case for further research in this area.</td><td>NIMHE to appoint programme lead and launch programme by autumn 2004</td></tr>
<tr><td>2) Action in schools</td><td>Resources to raise awareness of stigma and discrimination towards people with mental health problems, including a focus on ethnicity and gender, will be piloted and made available by the Department for Education and Skills (DfES) on Teachernet for use within Personal, Social and Health Education in schools. NIMHE's anti-stigma programme will work to make available practical support to primary and secondary schools and local education authorities at local level.

The issue of stigma and discrimination towards people with mental health problems will also be addressed through the Healthy Schools Programme led by the Department of Health (DH) and DfES.</td><td>NIMHE with DfES by September 2005

DH/DfES by September 2005</td></tr>
<tr><td>3) Raise awareness of people's rights</td><td>NIMHE will work jointly with the Disability Rights Commission (DRC) to raise awareness among individuals and employers of the rights of people with mental health problems under the Disability Discrimination Act (DDA).

The government will continue to monitor the impact of the DDA, including in relation to people with mental health impairment.</td><td>NIMHE with the DRC from 2004

DWP/DRC</td></tr>
</table>

Action	Detail	Who and when
4) Promote best practice in the public sector	The draft Disability Discrimination Bill includes a proposed new public sector duty to promote equality of opportunity for all disabled people, including those with mental health conditions. The duty will apply to 43,000 public bodies. It is modelled on the existing race equality duty, and will require public bodies to think imaginatively about the needs of disabled people and the actions they can take to improve equality: for example, by redesigning business processes, considering the needs of disabled people when specifying contracts, or by evaluating the quality of service they offer disabled people and taking action to improve it. The DRC code of practice relating to the new duty will need to ensure that issues in relation to people with mental health problems are clearly reflected.	DRC Following Bill passage
	Central government departments will review their employment practices in light of the Cabinet Office's new toolkit on employment and disability that will include a section on mental health. This will support delivery of the Cabinet Office target for disabled people to make up 3 per cent of the senior civil service by 2004-05.	All departments during 2004
	DH will review international evidence on the role and efficacy of pre-employment health assessments, in order to devise an evidence-based system for use in the NHS (with potential application for other employers). DH is also monitoring implementation of its guidance on *Mental Health and Employment in the NHS.*	DH review to report by spring 2005

The role of health and social care services in tackling social exclusion

9. Being in work and maintaining social contacts improves mental health outcomes, prevents suicide and reduces reliance on health services. Effective mental health services will view rehabilitation and support for reintegration into the community as an integral part of their work.

10. This section sets out the role of health and social care services in tackling social exclusion, and is complemented by the actions in the next sections to be led by other government departments: action will be needed *across government* to improve the current experiences of people with mental health problems. The problems identified in this report cannot be solved by any one department or organisation acting in isolation.

11. Health and social care services invest £140 million each year in vocational and day services for adults with mental health problems. This investment could be used more effectively to implement international evidence on what works, while providing a range of services to meet different needs. A number of areas are already showing what can be achieved by setting up Individual Placement and Support schemes on the US model, and through closer joint working with local partners.

12. Early access to mental health services for everyone affected by mental health problems, regardless of age, ethnicity, gender, sexuality or social status, is essential to avoid the escalation of more intractable problems. Ensuring that the physical health needs of people with mental health problems are addressed will also help to tackle health inequalities. Action in these areas will link to work on the forthcoming White Paper on improving health.

13. Take-up of community care direct payments, which can support participation in community activities, is significantly lower for adults with mental health problems compared with other groups of disabled people. Further action is needed to raise awareness about take-up of direct payments.

Action	Detail	Who and when
5) Support on employment and social issues for people with severe mental health problems	The Department of Health (DH) will work through the National Institute for Mental Health in England (NIMHE) and in liaison with the Department for Work and Pensions to implement evidence-based practice, in particular Individual Placement and Support. This will include working towards access to an employment adviser for everyone with severe mental health problems. A range of vocational and day services will be needed to meet the needs of all individuals, including those with the most severe conditions (see also action point 6). Provision of vocational and social support will be embedded in the Care Programme Approach (CPA), with full involvement of the service user. This will include: • establishing employment status on admission to hospital, and supporting job retention; • promoting involvement of carers and families; • identifying a lead contact on vocational and social issues in secondary care teams; • strengthening links to key local partners, in particular Jobcentre Plus and education providers (see also action points 12, 13 and 17); • access to advice and support on benefits issues. Mental Health Trusts will work towards monitoring vocational outcomes for people on CPA and employment rates of people with mental health problems within their own organisation, building on existing good practice. This work will support implementation of the *Standards for Better Health* (published by DH for consultation in February 2004).	NIMHE to publish guidance for commissioners by end 2004

Action	Detail	Who and when
6) Transform day services into community resources that promote social inclusion through improved access to mainstream opportunities	DH will work through NIMHE to ensure that day services for people with severe mental health problems develop to provide for supported employment, occupation and mainstream social contact beyond the mental health system. This should include: • access to supported employment opportunities where appropriate; • person-centred provision that caters appropriately for the needs of all individuals, including those with the most severe mental health problems; • developing strong links and referral arrangements with community services and local partners; • providing befriending, advocacy or support to enable people to access local services (including childcare services); • involving people with mental health problems in service design and operation; • a focus on social inclusion and employment outcomes. Progress in service redesign will be monitored through the annual review of mental health services (the 'Autumn Assessment') by Local Implementation Teams.	NIMHE to publish guidance for commissioners by end 2004
7) Advice on employment and social issues through primary care	NIMHE will test models for providing vocational and social support in or linked to primary care, working in partnership with the Department for Work and Pensions (DWP) and the Department for Constitutional Affairs (DCA) who provide funding for local advice services. This work will target deprived neighbourhoods first, and will include: • testing the impact of different types of adviser or advocate, including models using support time & recovery workers and the voluntary sector (drawing on the proposals for connected care centres[388]); • support to retain employment from the first request for sickness certification, including advice on the health impact of not working and liaison with the employer where appropriate; • a focus on moving clients towards mainstream services – such as Jobcentre Plus, Citizens Advice Bureaux and other legal advice agencies; • identifying parental and family responsibilities and support needs; • linking to learning, arts and exercise on prescription schemes; • using IT (for example adapting desk-top systems) and booklets to disseminate information in primary care settings; • measuring the impact of interventions on vocational and social outcomes; • developing quality standards for advice in primary care.	NIMHE with DCA/DWP from 2004

Action	Detail	Who and when
8) Strengthen training on vocational and social issues for health and social care professionals	NIMHE will work in collaboration with the NHS University, Workforce Development Confederations and Strategic Health Authorities, Skills for Health, the Training Organisation for Personal Social Services, higher and further education institutions, professional bodies and employers to:	NIMHE in collaboration with partner organisations
	• ensure that the new mental health workforce (including support time & recovery, primary care, carer support and community workers) undertake specific training in relation to employment and social inclusion issues as defined by local needs, supported where appropriate by the *Changing Workforce Programme*;	by end 2006
	• develop employment and social inclusion training for other health and social care staff and teams as defined by local needs;	by April 2007
	• implement in pre- and post-qualification training curricula the Ten Essential Shared Capabilities Framework and other relevant competency Frameworks, in particular the National Occupational Standards for mental health and the Knowledge Skills Framework for mental health staff (including drug and alcohol professionals). This will ensure that vocational and social inclusion issues are better reflected, including meeting the needs of ethnic minorities and people with complex needs;	by April 2007
	• develop the NIMHE Primary Care *Core Skills'* Programme for GPs and other primary care staff in partnership with the National Primary Care Development Team. This could include collaborative approaches for local and national application.	by September 2005
	All training needs to include the active involvement of people with mental health problems and carers.	
9) Tackle inequalities in access to health services	The Disability Rights Commission (DRC) will undertake a formal investigation of the physical health inequalities experienced by people with mental health problems.	DRC to complete review by 2006
	The Healthcare Commission (HC) will explore in collaboration with DH the scope for development of a waiting times indicator for psychological therapy, to be included in the trust performance indicator set in the future.	HC by 2005
	The National Treatment Agency (NTA) will conduct a review of access to and effectiveness of treatment and care for adults with co-morbid drug use and mild-moderate mental health problems, including meeting the needs of ethnic minorities, and develop improved performance indicators for these services.	NTA by summer 2005
	Research will be commissioned to develop evidence-based, practical ways of overcoming the barriers to accessing mental health services for people who are homeless or in temporary accommodation.	DH research to report by 2005
	The Department for the Environment, Food and Rural Affairs (DEFRA) will address mental health and social exclusion in rural areas through development of its Rural Stress Action Plan.	DEFRA from 2004

Action	Detail	Who and when
10) Promote greater take-up of direct payments to facilitate social participation	NIMHE will work with the voluntary sector to disseminate a guide to action on direct payments for adults with mental health problems for commissioners, managers, practitioners and people with mental health problems. This will include highlighting the potential for direct payments to help meet the needs of ethnic minorities and carers.	NIMHE by end 2004
	The Social Care Institute for Excellence (SCIE) will identify and disseminate good practice examples.	SCIE by end 2005
	DH will review the direct payment exclusion criteria in relation to people detained under mental health legislation on leave of absence from hospital.	DH by end 2005
11) Criminal justice and mental health	NIMHE and the Home Office (HO) will work together to develop a model to address coercive and complex pathways into and out of care for some ethnic minority groups, and to ensure that these groups are dealt with appropriately and responsively by both services. This will be informed by a mapping of existing good practice across the country, and will also consider gender issues.	NIMHE/HO to develop model by 2006
	Building on the forthcoming action plan on reducing re-offending, the HO and DH will work together to develop a pathways approach that can be used at local level to ensure that offenders with mental health problems are able to access suitable treatment at the earliest possible stage. As a first step NIMHE will identify current best practice and will actively support local areas in implementation.	NIMHE by end 2005
	NIMHE and the Probation Service will work towards making work-based mental health awareness training available for all probation officers. The training will be based on the successful programme currently being delivered to prison staff, which increases skills in responding appropriately to people with mental health problems. The training will cover diversity issues, including ethnicity and gender.	NIMHE and the Probation Service from 2004-05
	The Association of Chief Police Officers (ACPO) will review the available post-foundation training on mental health awareness, and ensure that ethnicity issues are fully addressed within it.	ACPO by June 2006
	The Central Police Training and Development Authority will make available Home Office funded mental health awareness training, in collaboration with NIMHE, at a number of regional centres.	Central Police Training and Development Authority by June 2007

Employment

14. Although many people with mental health problems want to work, the Social Exclusion Unit's consultation highlighted the widespread view that current systems are not sufficiently flexible to enable this as effectively as they could. Mental health services, Jobcentre Plus, local voluntary sector organisations and employers themselves all have a role to play in ensuring that people have real opportunities for work.

Action	Detail	Who and when
12) Improving access to employment programmes	***Pathways to Work* incapacity benefits reform pilots** were launched in October 2003 and extended to four more areas in April. The pilots offer a comprehensive package of return to work support, including specialist advisers, new programmes and better financial incentives such as the return to work credit of £40 per week. Additional funding was secured in Budget 2004 to extend work-focused interviews to existing Incapacity Benefit claimants in the pilot areas and provide a job preparation premium of £20 a week. DWP will make a decision about the future roll-out of the *Pathways to Work* pilots in light of the evaluation outcomes. The specific needs of adults with mental health problems will be addressed by: • testing the impact of longer periods of support following return to work; and • building strengthened partnerships between Jobcentre Plus and mental health services, including provision of outreach advice on employment in health settings.	DWP with DH from 2004
	The Department of Health will commission research on the Condition Management Programmes (CMP) to complement DWP's evaluation. This will look at changes in health status attributable to participation in the CMP, the use of health services, and issues such as health gain and public benefit.	DH from 2004
	Jobcentre Plus will implement improved **training** for Incapacity Benefit personal advisers on mental health issues, using experience from the *Pathways to Work* pilots; and through this raise awareness of issues for customers with mental health problems in all Jobcentre Plus offices.	Jobcentre Plus by 2005
	DWP will improve the clarity of guidance on the use of ***Access to Work*** to fund adjustments for people with mental health problems.	DWP by end 2004
	DWP will consider the scope to improve access to employment programmes, including the ***New Deal* programmes**, for people with mental health problems. This will include consideration of the National Employment Panel's recommendations to strengthen incentives for Jobcentre Plus to support disadvantaged clients, tailor support to individual need and make better use of the voluntary sector's expertise. It will also include the scope for greater consultation with people with experience of mental health problems.	DWP by end 2004

Action	Detail	Who and when
13) Easing the transition from benefits to work	DWP will improve awareness of the continuing needs of **Disability Living Allowance** (DLA) claimants upon returning to work; and review and revise DWP communications to ensure that staff and customers are aware of the circumstances in which someone is eligible for DLA, in particular that eligibility does not depend on someone being out of work.	DWP by 2005
	DWP will consider the feasibility of making the Incapacity Benefit ***linking rules*** more flexible, for example by allowing automatic registration and a faster return to work after using the linking rules.	DWP by 2005
	DWP will continue to monitor the impact of the Housing Benefit/Council Tax Benefit rapid reclaim form, which is designed to encourage more people to make the transition into work, and will keep this under review.	DWP from 2004
	The evaluation of the ***Permitted Work Rules*** will inform their future design. DWP will continue to work to raise awareness of the current arrangements to support people to increase their working hours to 16 or more hours per week, and will keep under review the case for further measures to facilitate this.	Evaluation to be published by end 2004
	DWP will consider whether there are additional channels via DH or mental health stakeholders for distributing **publicity materials** which describe benefit rules, employment programmes and how to access them through Jobcentre Plus; and keep the materials under review to ensure they effectively communicate key messages to disabled people, including people with mental health problems.	DWP with DH by 2005
14) Promoting enterprise and self-employment	The Department of Trade and Industry's Small Business Service (SBS) will pilot measures to improve the quality of support for adults with mental health problems, including people from ethnic minority groups, who wish to pursue enterprise and self-employment. This will be funded by £1.5 million from the Phoenix Fund over two years in collaboration with other government departments.	SBS from 2004

Action	Detail	Who and when
15) Supporting and engaging employers of all sizes, and promoting job retention	The NIMHE anti-stigma programme (see action point one) will develop ways of **supporting private and voluntary sector employers** to enable them to have access to the resources and support they need to act responsibly and supportively for people with mental health problems.	NIMHE to launch programme by autumn 2004
	The Health and Safety Executive (HSE) will expand its pilot programme to test different ways of supporting **small and medium enterprises** to improve health and safety at work.	HSE from 2004
	HSE will publish new management standards for employers aimed at preventing **work-related stress**.	New standards to be published by end 2004
	New HSE vocational rehabilitation guidance will advise employers on **job retention** for their ill, injured or disabled employees, including those with mental health problems.	Guidance published by autumn 2004
	DWP is working with DH to develop a **Framework for Vocational Rehabilitation** that will provide users and service providers with strategic direction and provide evidence of what works; and will consider lessons learned from the Job Retention and Rehabilitation Pilots.	DWP/DH framework published by autumn 2004
	DWP is developing an **employer engagement strategy**, working closely with employers and their representative organisations, to explore how best to increase the recruitment and retention of disabled people.	DWP from 2004

Supporting families and community participation

15. While work is very important to many people with mental health problems, their aspirations – just as for anyone else – extend much more broadly than this. They will have relationships and family responsibilities that are important to them, and they will want to take part in community life. Parents need support and recognition of their responsibilities, and their children's needs must also be addressed. As reflected in action point 5, involvement of carers and families within the Care Programme Approach should be promoted.

16. Activities such as education, arts, sports and volunteering can provide a useful stepping stone into work, but these and other activities can also be important in their own right and promote better mental health outcomes.

Action	Detail	Who and when
16) Better support for parents and their children	DH will commission the Social Care Institute for Excellence (SCIE) to conduct a systematic review of evidence and existing practice by health and social care services in supporting parents with mental health problems with their parenting needs, including meeting the needs of ethnic minority parents; and to publish new guidelines. In developing these guidelines, SCIE will, if appropriate, collaborate with the National Institute for Clinical Excellence.	SCIE from early 2005
	DfES will work with DH to ensure that the common core of training for professionals working with children and families addresses mental health issues.	DfES/DH from 2004
	DfES will encourage the emerging local structures for children and families' services to take explicit account of the needs of parents with mental health problems and their children, and collaborate locally with adult mental health services. DfES will work with DH to help develop greater awareness in adult mental health services of the need to support parents with mental health problems in their role as parents.	DfES/DH from 2004
	DfES will help improve access to family and parenting support by: • highlighting the needs of parents with mental health problems and their children in the emerging family policy strategy; and • encouraging local Sure Start programmes, children's centres, other early years settings and other local statutory and voluntary services such as Home Start to be accessible and to reach out to and support parents with mental health problems and respond to their needs and those of their children.	DfES from 2004
	DH will give priority and seek appropriate funding for a review of the quality of and access to family visiting facilities within hospitals, and general attitudes towards family visiting and young carers when a parent is in hospital.	Review to be undertaken by 2006
17) Promote access to adult learning, further and higher education	The Department for Education and Skills (DfES) will work with the Learning and Skills Council to disseminate good practice on supporting access to adult learning and further education for learners with mental health problems, for example by: • seeking a reference in the next grant letter to steer the Learning and Skills Council to address the needs of people with mental health problems; • including a reference to people with mental health problems in the Learning and Skills Council's forthcoming Equality and Diversity Strategy; and • ensuring that any new guidance in 2005-06 on learner support funding for adults addresses the needs of adults with mental health problems as with any other disability.	DfES from 2004

Action	Detail	Who and when
	DfES will support the newly formed Universities UK/SCOP Committee for the Promotion of Mental Well-being in Higher Education in developing a forward work plan to: • raise awareness of mental health issues; • disseminate good practice on supporting access to higher education for potential students with mental health problems; and • deliver effective support for students while in higher education. DfES will build on recent work on the Disabled Students' Allowance scheme to increase recognition and understanding by local education authorities and centre assessors of issues facing learners with mental health problems and standardise assessment procedures. Further and higher education institutions will review and make appropriate adjustments to their systems for raising awareness among all staff about issues for students with mental health problems, to ensure that no student is disadvantaged in their access to learning and services.	
18) Promote access to volunteering and arts opportunities	Models to enable adults with mental health problems to participate in volunteering are being developed through Capital Volunteering, a partnership project in London led by Community Service Volunteers and the National Institute for Mental Health in England (NIMHE). This is funded from HM Treasury's Invest to Save fund with £2.6 million allocated for the first stage (and a further £4.7 million available). The Department for Culture, Media and Sport (DCMS) in partnership with the Department of Health (DH) will give priority to undertaking research to establish the health benefits and social outcomes of participation in arts projects and the characteristics of effective local projects.	Community Service Volunteers/ NIMHE from 2004 DCMS/DH to report by end 2006
19) Effective interventions for young people	DfES will disseminate guidance on the role of Connexions Partnerships in supporting young people with mental health problems to stay in learning or find work, including closer liaison with Child and Adolescent Mental Health Services and adult mental health services to ensure effective early intervention building on the good practice developed in Hull. The forthcoming Children's National Service Framework will include measures to develop mental health services appropriate for adolescents, smooth the transition into adult services, and will include reference to the importance of maintaining a strong focus on vocational and social issues.	DfES by 2005 DH by 2004

Action	Detail	Who and when
20) Remove barriers to community roles	DfES, in partnership with local education authorities, will disseminate and clarify the school governors' regulations revised as a result of this project.	DfES from 2004
	The Home Office (HO) and Department for Constitutional Affairs (DCA), with advice from DH, will consult on modernising current eligibility criteria for jury service which exclude many adults with mental health problems.	HO/DCA by spring 2005
	NIMHE will promote more consistent practice on paying people with experience of mental health problems to advise on health service design, and will work with DWP to raise awareness of what payments can be made under the permitted work rules.	NIMHE with DWP by end 2004

Getting the basics right

17. Decent housing, financial stability and affordable transport are the essential building blocks without which people are unable to fulfil their aspirations. Increasing numbers of adults with mental health problems are homeless or have housing difficulties, and many report problems with transport services. Debt is a common problem, and people can struggle to access financial and legal advice services.

Action	Detail	Who and when
21) Decent homes	The Office of the Deputy Prime Minister (ODPM) and the Housing Corporation will identify best practice and draw up guidance for local authorities and registered social landlords on **preventing and managing rent arrears** which reflects the needs of vulnerable tenants, including people with mental health problems, in mainstream housing. This will cover issues such as early intervention and access to information and support to enable tenants to sustain their tenancies.	ODPM by spring 2005
	Good practice guidance on **Choice-Based Lettings** will address how vulnerable people – including those with mental health problems and from ethnic minorities – can be assisted and supported in making appropriate housing choices. ODPM will consider the need to issue further guidance on appropriate allocations when the current NIMHE/Housing Corporation research reports in summer 2004.	
	In revising the Code of Guidance on Homelessness, ODPM will ensure that it reflects homelessness and mental health issues.	
	ODPM will work with the Chartered Institute of Housing to ensure that mental health awareness is fully reflected in mainstream **education and training for housing professionals**.	

Action	Detail	Who and when
22) Access to transport	Access to transport to enable adults with mental health problems to travel to the services they need will be improved by: • reflecting the specific needs of adults with mental health problems within Local Transport Plan and Accessibility Planning guidance; and • considering the case for revisions to the statutory guidance to local authorities on giving concessionary travel to this group, in consultation with the Disabled Person's Transport Advisory Committee and other user groups.	Department for Transport in summer 2004 by end 2004
23) Access to financial and legal advice	The Department for Constitutional Affairs (DCA) and the Legal Services Commission will pilot new contracting arrangements for the delivery of advice services to people with mental health problems. This will re-focus provision on easier access to services which advise individuals on their rights, both during a stay in hospital and in the community, and will ensure that the needs of ethnic minorities are met.	DCA/Legal Services Commission to consult in 2004 and implement pilots by summer 2005

Making it happen

18. Significant improvement in opportunities and outcomes for people with mental health problems can only be achieved through closer partnership between organisations at national, regional and local level. It is essential that services are designed around the needs and aspirations of individuals, and not for the convenience of organisations.

19. Successful implementation of this action plan will require strong leadership at national and local level. There will need to be a major effort to disseminate good practice and evidence of what works more consistently across the country. A priority will be to make better use of the voluntary sector's expertise in tackling social exclusion, and support development of more effective commissioning practice.

Action	Detail	Who and when
24) National co-ordination	Set up a **cross-government implementation team** based within the National Institute for Mental Health in England (NIMHE) to drive forward delivery of this action plan. This will include secondees from other departments to maintain a cross-government focus. The **Ministers for Mental Health, Disabled People and Social Exclusion** will jointly oversee progress, reporting to the Cabinet Sub-Committee on Social Exclusion and Regeneration. Implementation will be co-ordinated through the **cross-government network** that has developed this report, to be jointly chaired by senior Department of Health and Department for Work and Pensions officials; and mainstreamed within Departments' overall delivery plans. There will also be formal links between the implementation team, the anti-stigma programme lead and the Department of Health's black and minority ethnic mental health programme.	NIMHE team to be in place by September 2004
25) Independent advisory group	An independent advisory group will be set up to advise the government on progress and contribute to implementation. The group will report to ministers through the Department of Health (DH) Mental Health Taskforce, and will include representation from the full range of relevant sectors and people with experience of mental health problems. The group will publish an independent report on progress every year.	DH by autumn 2004 First published report summer 2005
26) Local implementation (see also paragraphs 20-26 below)	Implementation at local level will be led jointly by the primary care trust and local authority. They will work in close partnership with the mental health trust, local Patient and Public Involvement Forums, and Jobcentre Plus. They will ensure that implementation is mainstreamed within the local strategic partnership delivery arrangements. NIMHE will provide practical support for implementation through its Regional Development Centres, including a national conference to launch implementation and through establishment of networks on key implementation themes. The Social Exclusion Unit (SEU), in partnership with NIMHE and other departments, will disseminate a pack of fact sheets summarising this report and providing practical advice on implementation for practitioners in different sectors.	PCTs and local authorities from 2004 NIMHE from 2004 SEU/NIMHE by September 2004

Action	Detail	Who and when
27) Monitor progress (see also paragraphs 27-33)	The implementation team will monitor progress in increasing the employment rate of people with mental health problems towards the rate for the general population, and improving access to services and opportunities for community participation. Monitoring information will be published in the annual progress report.	NIMHE from 2004
	The new joint review inspection framework being developed by the Healthcare Commission and Commission for Social Care Improvement (HC/CSCI) will reflect vocational and social inclusion issues.	HC/CSCI to pilot new framework by spring 2005
	Work on mental health within the shared priorities theme on healthier communities/health inequalities is to be reflected in the new performance framework for local authorities being developed by the Office of the Deputy Prime Minister (ODPM) and the Audit Commission.	ODPM by 2005
	The Adult Learning Inspectorate (ALI) will make a clear distinction between outcomes for people with different disabilities, including people with mental health problems, in all relevant inspection reports about the quality of provision.	ALI from April 2005
	DH will work with other departments to evaluate the impact of this action plan, and to further develop the evidence base for interventions to tackle social exclusion among people with mental health problems. This will include measuring social outcomes such as employment in all future mental health effectiveness studies.	DH from 2004

Local implementation

20. Local implementation is the joint responsibility of primary care trusts and local authorities, working in close partnership with the Mental Health Trust and Jobcentre Plus. The other key local partners who need to be involved in implementation are:

- people with experience of mental health problems and carers;
- voluntary, community and private sector service providers;
- local employers;
- Learning and Skills Councils; and
- Connexions.

21. The Primary Care Trust Chief Executive and the local authority Director of Social Services, in conjunction with other local authority departments, have lead responsibility for drawing up a local action plan to implement the measures in this report. This will include reviewing current commissioning practices to ensure that participation of the voluntary and community sectors is maximised. It may be appropriate for this work to be co-ordinated through the existing mental health Local Implementation Team.

22. Local agencies will ensure that implementation is mainstreamed within the local strategic partnership's delivery arrangements. Through the partner agencies, the existing local strategic partnership theme groups (for example on employment, health or housing) will take individual responsibility for ensuring delivery. Mental health is already being addressed in some areas through local strategic partnerships and local neighbourhood renewal strategies, for example in Nottingham where one of the local strategic partnership's performance indicators relates to mental health.

***WorkNet*, Bromley, London**

WorkNet was set up in 2001 and has ten partner organisations[389] across the voluntary and statutory sectors, all working in the fields of education and employment. It promotes a range of services for people experiencing mental health problems to give them the opportunity to access paid employment or further education.

The network receives 38 per cent of its funding from the European Social Fund and the remainder from its partner organisations. The majority of referrals come from the area's three community mental health teams, which hold fortnightly drop-in sessions. Once someone is in contact with the network, partners will refer through to each other and ensure that the next step is secured before someone finishes their current activities. Monthly steering meetings reinforce these links.

Funding

23. Departments have incorporated the actions set out in this plan within their business plans for the current financial year. For example, the new anti-stigma programme is backed by £1.1 million investment from the Department of Health. The Small Business Service has made £1.5 million available from the Phoenix Fund to be invested over two years, and the Home Office and National Institute for Mental Health in England have jointly identified up to £155,000 to strengthen police training. Investment for future years will be determined by the outcome of the current spending review.

24. Sources of funding made available by the Department of Health to support implementation, in addition to mainstream health and social care budgets, include:

- **£22 million ringfenced capital funding** for local councils with social services responsibilities to support the costs associated with implementing this report;[390]
- the **Mental Health Grant:** one of the priorities for the Mental Health Grant in 2004-05 for local councils with social services responsibilities is to provide a range of rehabilitation and support services, including respite care and employment-oriented services, which promote social inclusion and independence;[391] and
- the **Section 64 Grant:** implementation of this report and work to address ethnic minority mental health are funding priorities for 2005-06 for the Section 64 Grant, which provides the greatest single source of financial support for the voluntary sector from the Department of Health.

25. Other relevant sources of funding to support implementation of this report include Jobcentre Plus, Learning and Skills Councils and Local Strategic Partnerships. The website www.governmentfunding.org.uk provides information on grants that are available to voluntary and community groups from the Home Office, Department for Education and Skills, Department of Health and the Office of the Deputy Prime Minister.

Regional co-ordination

26. The **regional social inclusion leads** in NIMHE's Regional Development Centres will drive forward implementation at regional level, supported by the national implementation team. Leads are already in place in each of the regions, and full-time appointments will be made for this role wherever possible. They will work closely with NIMHE's regional anti-stigma/discrimination and mental health promotion leads (funded by the anti-stigma programme), and their role will include:

- developing strong partnerships with relevant structures at regional level, in particular the Government Office for the Regions, Regional Development Agencies and Jobcentre Plus;
- providing support and assistance to primary care trusts, mental health trusts and local authorities;
- monitoring progress towards developing socially inclusive practice as set out in this report's action plan;
- disseminating examples of good practice and evidence of what works;
- promoting effective commissioning practice, in particular greater involvement of the voluntary and community sectors in providing services; and
- liaising with strategic health authorities who have responsibility for performance management of primary care trusts and mental health services.

Monitoring progress

27. The implementation team will monitor progress towards the government's objectives as set out in this report using a series of indicators (see Annex C). Data for the indicators will primarily be drawn from existing sources of information. The indicators will include monitoring progress in relation to:

- reducing stigma and discrimination towards people with mental health problems;
- increasing the employment rate for people with mental health problems;
- income growth for people with mental health problems on the lowest incomes;
- reducing homelessness and improving educational outcomes; and
- increasing participation in the community and social networks.

28. This data will be made publicly available through NIMHE's website, and will be published annually as part of the independent advisory group's annual report.

29. As set out in the action plan, vocational and social outcomes for people with mental health problems will be monitored through the NHS and local government performance management systems.

30. In addition, the Adult Learning Inspectorate will distinguish in all relevant inspection reports the quality of provision for learners with different disabilities including people with mental health conditions. This will include reporting on the numbers of people with mental health needs on programmes, and the quality of provision including achievements such as success in finding and sustaining employment. This will enable a baseline to be established and ongoing progress over time to be measured.

Strengthening the evidence base

31. A range of data sources already exist, in particular the Psychiatric Morbidity Survey and the Labour Force Survey, which provide important information about mental health and social exclusion. However, this project has identified a number of limitations in the availability of data:

- data from social surveys and government cannot always be disaggregated by disability, impairment or health problem;
- there is a lack of consistency, preciseness and validity in how research studies, social surveys and monitoring systems measure mental health problems;
- studies which set out specifically to assess prevalence of mental health problems contain limited consideration of social inclusion issues; and
- up-to-date, reliable and long-term evidence is not always available due to limited sources of longitudinal data and the infrequency of some national surveys.

32. The Department for Work and Pensions is commissioning an independent feasibility study to assess how long-term information needs on health and disability can be met. This will consider whether better information can be collected on people with mental health problems and the experience of this group in relation to areas such as employment, education, income, use of services, social participation and benefits. It will also consider the possibility of collecting data over time to improve evidence on the onset, severity and trajectories of mental health problems over lifetimes. In addition, this would provide better information on the co-occurrence of mental health problems alongside other disability and health problems. The findings from the feasibility study will be published in mid-2004.

33. This project has identified three priorities in relation to future research, evaluation and monitoring.

- There is a need to develop the approach to measuring mental health problems within national surveys through standardised, validated tools to screen for mental health problems, and harmonisation of existing standard disability indicators. The Department for Work and Pension is co-ordinating cross-government work to harmonise the questions asked about long-standing disability or illness (including mental illness) which may limit work-related or other activity. This is expected to include an examination of impairment-specific definitions used in surveys. Preliminary analysis for the SEU suggested that the long-standing illness question in the Psychiatric Morbidity Survey only identified between a third and a half of adults assessed as having a mental health problem using screening tools.[392]
- It is important that all research into the effectiveness of mental health services considers the impact of services, approaches and interventions on social inclusion outcomes (e.g. work, housing, community participation and social networks). There is also scope for better use of data collected through the Psychiatric Morbidity Surveys commissioned by the Department of Health to measure changes in social inclusion outcomes over time.
- As outlined in the action plan, the project has identified a number of specific areas in which further research is needed to improve the evidence base for interventions to tackle mental health and social exclusion. The Department of Health will give priority and seek appropriate sources of funding to undertake these studies.

ANNEX A: Summary of consultation findings

1. Consultation questionnaires were sent in May 2003 to people with mental health problems, health and social care bodies, professional and voluntary organisations, local authorities and those providing housing, employment and benefit support. 912 responses were received. The three largest groups of respondents were public sector workers, people with mental health problems and carers, and voluntary sector representatives. Table 1 below lists the issues most frequently mentioned by respondents.[393]

Table 1: Top 10 issues by percentage of respondents who raised them

	%
Impact of stigma/lack of understanding of mental health issues	83
Support to gain employment/overcoming barriers to getting a job	72
Benefits issues	62
Lack of social networks, access to social activities and day centres	53
Access to employment more generally	53
Lack of self-confidence/social withdrawal by the individual	52
Education and awareness-raising of mental health issues	49
Employer-focused interventions	48
Access to recreation – leisure, sport, art/theatre, cafés, libraries	38
Mental health symptoms and medication side effects	34

2. Other issues raised included poverty and low income (28 per cent), access to and quality of housing (28 per cent), and practical issues such as access to transport and support with childcare (22 per cent).

3. Respondents identified a number of priority areas that they wanted the SEU project to address:

- tackling **stigma** and **increasing awareness** of mental health issues: within the workplace and among employers, mental health professionals, the general public and the media;
- improving access to **employment:** more employment schemes; easier access to training and education; support for job retention; and incentives, information, training and support for employers;
- further improvements to the **benefits system** to address problems with the complexity of the system, access to advice, and low income as a barrier to social participation;
- ensuring **access to mental health treatment and services:** high quality mental health services and treatment options; community integration, psycho-social interventions, recovery approaches and a reduced focus on medical intervention; increasing user involvement and including families and communities; earlier intervention; better partnerships across sectors; and more resources; and

- improving **social participation:** more funding to increase the opportunities available; more mentoring and befriending services; free memberships and discount rates; access to free co-ordinated transport; improving publicity about services; improving referral processes; and a single access point for all referrals to and information about services.

Consultation events

4. Seven regional consultation events across England were held in partnership with the National Institute for Mental Health in England to seek the views of people with mental health problems and carers. Participants gave their views through small group discussions, graffiti walls, postcards and questionnaires, and one-to-one talks with event facilitators. Approximately 500 people attended these events, and the majority were people with mental health problems.

5. The issues raised largely echoed the written consultation. Participants stressed the importance of government action to address stigma and barriers to work, and emphasised the value of services that are responsive to and driven by people with mental health problems and carers.

Local area studies

6. Four area studies in Bromley/Penge (London), Peterborough, Liverpool and Northumberland were undertaken to understand delivery issues better from a local perspective. The areas provided a range of demographic characteristics, deprivation levels, geographical spread and rural/urban mix. Meetings were held with people with mental health problems, carers, staff from statutory and voluntary sector health, social care, employment, housing and education services.

7. All areas had positive examples of services that promoted the social inclusion of people with mental health problems. Many projects were initiated and provided by the voluntary sector. In several areas, the involvement of people with mental health problems and carers in strategic planning was well developed. The emphasis on helping people find and keep jobs varied significantly. Variations were also noted in relation to the range of day activities funded by local providers.

8. Factors which had facilitated progress in developing initiatives included:

- **leadership and planning:** strong leadership and local political support; effective strategic planning across sectors; and, in particular, positive working relationships between statutory and voluntary sector agencies;

- **community involvement:** active service user groups at grass-roots level; projects which built on capacity within local communities;

- staff **commitment** and **enthusiasm** to make things happen;

- **underpinning philosophy** of outreach, rights-based, holistic approaches as opposed to a focus on symptom reduction and risk management; and

- **performance management:** in two areas, critical service review had provided impetus to take action.

9. A number of potential barriers to making further progress at local level were identified.

- **Contextual issues:** local socio-economic factors (such as high cost of living or the availability of jobs), geographic factors (for example large rural areas) and historical factors could hinder progress.

- **Priorities:** it was felt that tackling social exclusion among adults with mental health problems did not feature strongly in national delivery priorities; at the local level, agendas were dominated by the need to achieve existing National Service Framework milestones and targets.

- **Commissioning/strategic direction:** Primary Care Trust commissioning of mental health services was underdeveloped and often not seen as a priority. Providers tended to carry out ad hoc developments, resulting in service provision being patchy.

- **Inter-agency issues:** varying priorities for different agencies and sectors, lack of commitment from particular parts of the system, ineffective communication and compartmentalised services.

- **Resource issues:** lack of resources, budget cuts, monies being tied up in existing services, inequity in resource allocation, gaps in service provision and local infrastructure (such as transport and housing) as well as insecure/short-term funding of the voluntary sector.

- **Workforce issues:** difficulties in recruitment and retention of front line staff, limited knowledge of community resources, heavy workloads and attitudinal barriers.

ANNEX B: Social and financial costs

Figure 14: Social and financial costs associated with failure to prevent social exclusion among adults with mental health problems

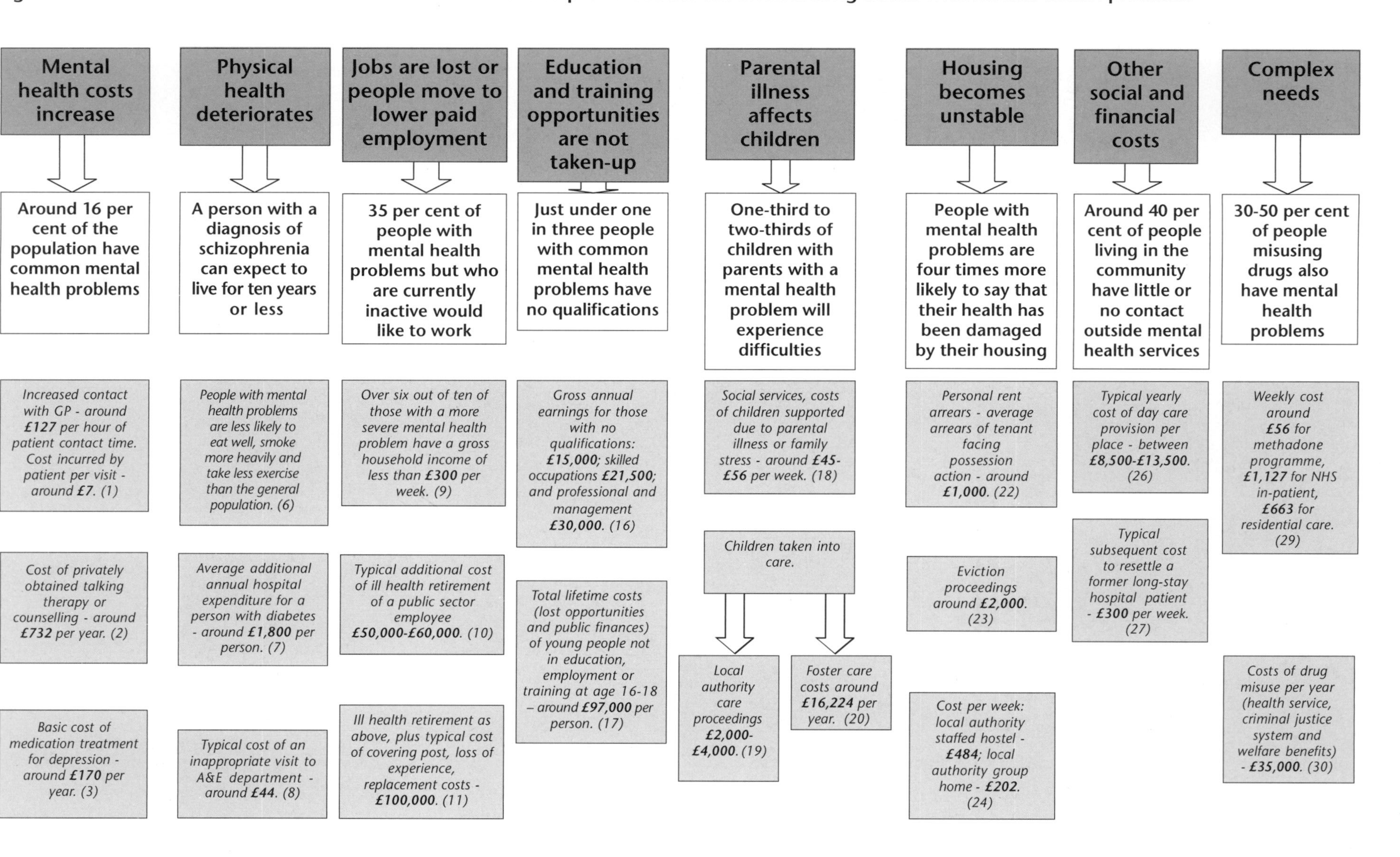

*Community Mental Health Team - around **£59** per hour of patient contact. Specialist community psychiatric nurse - around **£70** per hour patient contact. (4)*

*Cost per inpatient per day: NHS psychiatric intensive care unit - **£420**; acute psychiatric ward - **£165**; long-stay hospital **£141** Cost per average stay in intensive care unit - around **£5,169**. (5)*

*Direct and indirect costs of typical work-related stress absence - around **£5,500-£8,000** per case. (12)*

*Typical staff replacement costs: managers **£5,699**; clerical **£2,096**; average **£3,462**. (13)*

*Sheltered workshops specifically for people with mental health problems - cost per placement per year **£3,250-£8,700**. (14)*

*Single person on Incapacity Benefit will receive **£3,627** per year. (15)*

*Annual cost of care around **£31,000.** (21)*

*Complex need placements - up to **£1,200** per week. (25)*

*Example travel premium for a person with depression - **£307**. For a person without - **£17.60**. (28)*

1. A Netten and L Curtis, *Unit Costs of Health and Social Care 2003*, (Canterbury, Personal Social Services Research Unit, 2003)
2. Mind, *The Hidden Costs of Mental Health*, (London, Mind, 2003)
3. Department of Health, *Prescription Statistics*, 2003. (England only)
4. A Netten and L Curtis, *Unit Costs of Health and Social Care 2003*, (Canterbury, Personal Social Services Research Unit, 2003)
5. A Netten and L Curtis, *Unit Costs of Health and Social Care 2003*, (Canterbury, Personal Social Services Research Unit, 2003)
6. R McCreadie and C Kelly, 'Patients with schizophrenia who smoke: private disaster, public resource' Editorial, *British Journal of Psychiatry*, 176 (2002): 109
7. C J Currie et al, 'NHS Acute Sector Expenditure for D abetes: The Present, the Future and Excess In-patient cost of care', *Diabetic Medicine* Vol 14, No 8, 1997
8. Shelter, *Go Home and Rest? The use of an accident and emergency department by homeless people*, (London, Shelter, 1996)
9. Office for National Statistics, *The Social and Economic Circumstances of Adults with Mental Disorders*, (London, Office for National Statistics, 2002)
10. Her Majesty's Treasury, *Review of ill health retirement in the public sector* (London, Her Majesty's Treasury, 2000)
11. Her Majesty's Treasury, *Review of ill health retirement in the public sector* (London, Her Majesty's Treasury, 2000)
12. Health and Safety Executive, Ill Health Cost Calculator, www.hse.gov.uk
13. Health and Safety Executive, Ill Health Cost Calculator, www.hse.gov.uk
14. A Netten and L Curtis, *Unit Costs of Health and Social Care 2003*, (Canterbury, Personal Social Services Research Unit, 2003)
15. Department for Work and Pensions, internally produced figures, 2004
16. Department for Education and Skills website, Trends in Education and Skills (www.dfes.gov.uk), 2004
17. C Godfrey, S Hutton, J Bradshaw, B Coles, G Craig and J Johnson, *Estimating the Cost of Being 'Not in Education, Employment or Training at Age 16-18'*, (London, Department for Education and Skills, 2002)
18. A Netten and L Curtis, *Unit Costs of Health and Social Care 2003*, (Canterbury, Personal Social Services Research Unit, 2003)
19. Audit Commission, *Misspent Youth*, (London, Audit Commission, 1996)
20. Social Exclusion Unit, *A Better Education for Children in Care*, (London, Office of the Deputy Prime Minister, 2003)
21. Audit Commission, *Misspent Youth*, (London, Audit Commission, 1996)
22. Citizens' Advice Bureau, *Possession action - the last resort?* (London, Citizens' Advice Bureau, 2003)
23. Shelter, *House Keeping: Preventing homelessness through tackling rent arrears in social housing*, (London, Shelter, 2003)
24. A Netten and L Curtis, *Unit Costs of Health and Social Care 2003*, (Canterbury, Personal Social Services Research Unit, 2003)
25. A Netten and L Curtis, *Unit Costs of Health and Social Care 2003*, (Canterbury, Personal Social Services Research Unit, 2003)
26. A Netten and L Curtis, *Unit Costs of Health and Social Care 2003*, (Canterbury, Personal Social Services Research Unit, 2003)
27. A Netten and L Curtis, *Unit Costs of Health and Social Care 2003*, (Canterbury, Personal Social Services Research Unit, 2003)
28. Social Exclusion Unit web-based research, 2004
29. A Netten and L Curtis, *Unit Costs of Health and Social Care 2003*, (Canterbury, Personal Social Services Research Unit, 2003)
30. C Godfrey, G Eaton, C McDougall and A Culyer, *The economic and social cost of Class A drug use in England and Wales*, Home Office Research Study 249 (London, Home Office, 2000)

ANNEX C: Indicators to monitor progress

The following set of indicators will be used to monitor progress in implementing the action plan set out in the report. For each indicator, the national data source that will be used and the anticipated outcome of the report's action plan are outlined.

It should be noted that there are variations within the national data sources in relation to the measurement of mental health problems. The methods for measuring mental health problems and the implications of the variations will be made explicit in the reporting of the data in the annual implementation report.

Indicator	Data Source	Outcome
Stigma and discrimination		
i) Attitudes towards people with mental health problems	• Department of Health (DH) attitudes to mental illness survey (10 years) • Ofcom to monitor portrayal of mental health problems in broadcast media • Department for Work and Pensions (DWP) monitoring of employer attitudes • National Institute for Mental Health in England (NIMHE) baseline survey of service user experience	Positive shift in attitudes and behaviour
ii) Proportion of DDA-disabled adults with mental health problems aware that civil rights of disabled people are protected	DWP monitoring survey	Increase in proportion of people aware of their rights
Employment		
i) People with mental health problems in paid work	Labour Force Survey (LFS)	Year-on-year increase in numbers and proportion (subject to economic cycle)
Income and benefits		
i) Income growth for people with mental health problems with the lowest income	Psychiatric Morbidity Survey (PMS)	Decrease in proportion of people with mental health problems in lowest three income deciles
ii) Number of people with mental health problems on Incapacity Benefit on mental health grounds	Incapacity Benefit administrative data	Decrease in numbers and proportion

Indicator	Data Source	Outcome
Education		
i) Number of people with mental health problems with no qualifications	LFS/PMS	Decrease in numbers and proportion
iii) Number of people with mental health problems achieving a qualification equivalent to NVQ level 2	LFS/PMS	Increase in numbers and proportion
Housing		
i) Number of homeless people with mental health problems accepted as being in priority need for housing	Office of the Deputy Prime Minister (ODPM)	Year-on-year decrease in numbers
ii) Number of people with mental health problems assisted by the Supporting People programme	ODPM	Contextual information
Taking part in the local community		
i) Number of people with mental health problems that would have liked more leisure activity in the past year	PMS	Decrease in proportion
Social networks		
i) Size of primary support group	PMS	Decrease in the proportion of people with mental health problems whose primary support group is three or less
Direct payments		
i) Number of people with mental health problems in receipt of direct payments	DH Performance Assessment Framework (PAF) indicator	Year-on-year increase in numbers and proportion to narrow the gap in relation to other eligible groups

In addition, other national and local surveys and performance monitoring data will be drawn on to inform the assessment of progress in relation to these indicators and other action points contained within the report. In particular, local area data from the Labour Force Survey will be used to examine the breakdown by local authority of employment rates for people with mental health problems.

At local level, other data that could be useful to monitor progress include an upward trend in the:

- number of people on the Care Programme Approach (CPA) being supported in open employment;
- number of people on CPA being supported in mainstream education;
- number of people on CPA working as a volunteer; and
- number of people with mental health problems employed by mental health trusts, local authorities and other public sector bodies.

Annex D: Case study contact details

Chapter	Title	Name	Telephone	Email/Fax/Address	Website
1	Chinese Outreach Service	Andrew Wong	0114 2509594	info@kinhon.fsnet.co.uk	www.kinhon.fsnet.co.uk
1	Northumberland: GP Services	Frances Dower GP		The Rothbury Practice 3 Market Place Rothbury Northumberland NE65 7UW	
3	Sanity Fair	John Gibson		Johngibson.magmh@tiscali.co.uk	www.sanityfair.org.uk
3	Public Education Programme	Professor Julian Leff		Jleff@rfc.ucl.ac.uk	
3	Northumberland Police	Sergeant Jon Dowd	01661 868499	Community Safety Department Northumbria Police HQ North Road Ponteland Newcastle Upon Tyne NE20 OBL	
3	School Workshops Maidstone & Sevenoaks	Vanessa Pinfold	020 8547 9217	Vanessa.pinfold@rethink.org	www.rethink.org
3	Open Up	Maggie Gibbons	020 7700 8171	maggie.gibbons@mhmedia.com	www.mhmedia.com www.openuptoolkit.net
3	See Me	Linda Dunion	0131 624 8945	info@seemeescotland.org	www.seemescotland.org
4	Health Plus, Bradford	George Scully	01274 424780	george.scully@bradford.nhs.uk	
4	CPA Rotherham	Gillian Whall	01709 382118	Gillian.whall@rotherhampct.nhs.uk	
4	Antenna Outreach Service	Norma Johnson (Project info) Kwame Mckenzie (Medical/academic info)	Norma Johnson: 020 8365 9537	Antenna@outreachservice.fsnet.co.uk k.mckenzie@rfc.ucl.ac.uk	
4	Gateshead Council	Peter Lloyd	0191 4333000	plloyd@gateshead.gov.uk	
4	Mainstream, Liverpool	Jo Seddon or Sarah Ogden	0151 709 2366	imagine@mentalhealth.org.uk jo.seddon@imaginementalhealth.org.uk sogden@imaginementalhealth.org.uk	www.imaginementalhealth. org.uk
4	Cares of Life	Dr Dele Olajide		Dele.olajide@slam.nhs.uk	
4	Connexions	Kate Macdonald	07775 904 593	k.m.macdonald@hull.ac.uk	
4	PACE	Rosemary Watt-Wyness	020 7700 1323	Fax: 020 7609 4909	www.pacehealth.org.uk
4	REST	Chris Coates		ChrisCoatesREST@ruralnet.org.uk	

Chapter	Title	Name	Telephone	Email/Fax/Address	Website
4	Bromley Community Drugs Project	Pete Burkinshaw	020 8289 1999	pete.burkinshaw@turning-point.co.uk	
4	Redcar and Cleveland Mind Day Services	Sam Waites		Dove House 5 Turner Street Redcar TS10 main@randcmind.org	
4	HMP Birmingham	Charanjit Mehat	0121 345 2500 ex. 2375	Fax: 0121 345 2361 Charanjit.Mehat@hmps.gsi.gov.uk	
5	Safe and Healthy Working	Ann Halliday	0131 536 8775	ann.halliday@hebs.scot.nhs.uk	
5	SW London & St George's	Miles Rinaldi	020 8682 6929	Miles.Rinaldi@swlstg-tr.nhs.uk	
5	Making Space Options	Paul Dodd	01785 228622	staffordoptions@btconnect.com	
5	Six Mary's Place Guesthouse	Kevin Robbie	0131 539 7374	kevin.robbie@forthsector.org.uk	www.sixmarysplace.co.uk
5	First Step Trust	Ronnie Wilson Carole Furnivall	020 8855 7386	Ronnie@fst.org.uk Carole@fst.org.uk	
6	Pentreath Ltd, Cornwall	Louise Knox	01726 850565	louise@pentreath.co.uk	
6	BEAT – Action teams for jobs	Gail Jago Mandy Gardiner	01208 254282 Gail Jago: 07779 357319 Mandy Gardiner: 07779 357314	Fax No. 01208 254250 Gail.jago@jobcentreplus.gsi.gov.uk mandy.gardiner@dwp.gsi.gov.uk	
6	Enable Project	Jonathan Allan	01743 340035		www.shropshireonline.gov.uk/ ssenable.nsf
6	Job Retention BT	Jill Pearson	020 7356 5433	jill.pearson@bt.com	
6	Job Retention Avon & Wiltshire	Roger Butterworth	0117 963 3681	jobretentionteam@bristolswpct.nhs.uk	
7	Brent Black African & Caribbean MH Consortium	Deltine Patterson	020 8453 3419	Dpatterson@bbmhc@btconnect.com	
7	Family Welfare Association, Building Bridges	Rose De Paeztron	020 7272 4412	Rose.depaeztron@fwaprojects.org.uk	
7	Wigan FE College	Jill Mumford	01942 761 887/849	Mumfi@supanet.com	
7	College of NE London	Wendy Lanham	020 8442 3869	Wendy.Lanham@haringey.nhs.u	
7	Nottingham Trent University	Phil Scarffe	0115 8482536	Philip.scarffe@ntu.ac.uk	
7	SWAN Leisure Centre	David Bruce		swan.centre@leisureconnection.co.uk	
7	START	Wendy Teall Morag Musk	Wendy Teall 0161 257 0675 Morag Musk 0161 257 0510	Wendy.teall@mhsc.nhs.uk Morag.musk@mhsc.nhs.uk	
8	Look Ahead Housing	Chris Hampson		Chrishampson@lookahead.org.uk	
8	Assessment & Resettlement	Glynn Gunning	020 8313 4134	Glynn.gunning@bromley.gov.uk	
8	Cambridgeshire Advocacy	Mark Evans	01733 758278	Cias@btconnect.com	
8	Loonscape	Vyvyan Kinross		webmaster@loonscape.com	www.loonscape.com
9	Bromley WorkNet Forum	Kim Kelly	020 8461 7140	kim.kelly@bromley.gov.uk	www.worknetbromley.co.uk

Annex E: Acknowledgements

Unless otherwise stated, all quotes in this report are taken from the written consultations, the area studies or visits undertaken by members of the project team.

Area Studies

As part of its research, the Social Exclusion Unit (SEU) conducted area studies in four local areas: Bromley (London), Peterborough, Liverpool and Northumberland. This involved meetings with a variety of key people who worked with service users and included meetings with service users and carers. We are very grateful for the time and help they gave us, and for their openness and honesty in answering our questions.

Bromley

Health and Social Care: Horizon House, Oxleas Trust, Primary care/health development services, and Stepping Stones CMHT

Employment: Jobcentre Plus, LinkUp 2, Status Employment, and Worknet

Social Participation: Assertive Outreach Team, Bromley Mind, Broomleigh Housing Orpington College, Supporting People, and Turning Point

Liverpool

Health and Social Care: Assertive Outreach Team, Community Health Council, Mersey Care NHS Trust, Windsor Road In-patient Facility, Windsor Road CMHT, and Windsor Road Stakeholder Group

Employment: Access to Employment – Mersey Care NHS Trust, Network Employment, and WHSmith

Social Participation: Community Care Housing, Consortium, Crown Street Resource Centre, Citizens' Advice Bureau – Income Maximisation Scheme, Family Welfare Association, Homeless Outreach Team, Mainstream, Mary Seacole House, Queer Notions, Rethink Advocacy, Supporting People, Whitechapel Centre, and YMCA

Northumberland

Health and Social Care: Newcastle, North Tyneside and Northumberland Mental Health NHS Trust, Alnwick Day and Outreach, Local GP, Northern Causeway, and North Health Promotion

Employment: Berwick Jobcentre

Social Participation: Berwick Citizens Advice Bureau, Berwickshire Housing Association, Connexions, Learning and Skills Council, Morpeth Citizens Advice Bureau, Northumberland College, Northumberland County Council (Transport), North Northumberland Voluntary Action, Supporting People, Swan Leisure Centre, Turning Point, and User Voice

Peterborough

Health and Social Care: Assertive Outreach Team, Child and Adolescent Mental Health Services, Carer Support Services, District General Hospital In-Patient Unit, Local GP, Mental Health Assessment Team, New Haven Hostel, Occupational Therapy Team, Rehabilitation Team, Sahara Community Care Services and Youth Offending Team

Employment: Jobcentre Plus Disability Employment Adviser and Richmond Fellowship

Social Participation: Adult Learning Service, Citizens Advice Bureau, Community Learning Disability Team, Gladca Community Association, Mohamed Kassamali (faith leader), Mosaic Day Centre, Peterborough Advocacy Service, Peterborough and Fenland MIND, Peterborough Council for Voluntary Service, Salvation Army, and Supporting People

Visits

In addition to the area studies, the SEU visited a number of local authorities and organisations across the United Kingdom. We are very grateful for their help with the project.

Antenna, London
Assertive Outreach Team, Bradford
Avon & Wiltshire Mental Health Partnerships Job Retention Team
Barnet College, London
Blipart Internet Café, Birmingham
Breaking Barriers, Peterborough
Bridges to Education, Chelmsford, Essex
Bridges to Work, Chelmsford, Essex
Burgh Lodge, Fife
Cares of Life, Southwark, London
Chelmsford Personal Development Service, Essex
Circle of Friends, Warwickshire
College Link Programme, London
Cwmbwrla Day Centre, Swansea
Enable Employment Project, Shropshire
Falcon House Clubhouse for the Deaf, London
Family Welfare Association, Building Bridges, Lewisham, London
Family Welfare Association, Tower Hamlets, London
Fife Employment Access Trust (FEAT), Fife
First Step Trust Lambeth, London
Flourish House, Glasgow
Hackney Mind, London
Hafal drop-in centre, Swansea
HealthPlus, Bradford
HMP Birmingham
HOPE, Cornwall
Isledon Resource Centre, London
Keeping the Family in Mind Project, Barnardo's Action with Young Carers Project, Liverpool
Making Space, Lancashire
Making Space – 'Options', Staffordshire
Mayfair Centre, Shropshire
Mental Health Matters, Tyneside
Mind, Dacorum
Northumbria Police, Northumbria
Nottingham Trent University, Nottingham

Oakleaf Enterprises, Surrey
Pentreath Industries Ltd, Cornwall
Portsmouth Interaction, Hampshire
Prescriptions for Learning, Nottingham
Prospects, Essex
Redcar and Cleveland Mind, Tyneside
Salford Mental Health Citizens Advice Bureau, Greater Manchester
Sheffield Care Trust Council, South Yorkshire
Six Mary's Place Guest House, Edinburgh
South West London and St George's Mental Health NHS Trust, London
Stonham Housing, Norwich
Sure Start West Green and Chestnuts, Haringey, London
Time Bank, South London & Maudsley NHS Trust, London
Trongate Studios, Glasgow
Victoria Park Café, Swansea
Waddington Street Centre, Durham
WellFamily Service, Family Welfare Association, Haringey, London
Wigan & Leigh FE College, Lancashire
Workways, Exeter
Youth Enquiry Service (YES), Plymouth

International visits

SEU officials went on visits to the US and Finland to learn about international best practice on mental health. We are grateful to the following organisations for their help.

US

Alternatives Unlimited Inc
American Association of Persons with Disabilities
Bazelon Centre
Bennington IPS project
Boston University, Centre for Psychiatric Rehabilitation
Career Resource Centre
Centre for Medical Health Services
National Council on Disability
New Hampshire Dartmouth Psychiatric Research Center
Supported and Residential Employment

Finland

Affinity – the Finnish Central Association for Mental Health
ALVI and ELVI Residential Homes
Half way House: Drugs and Alcohol Rehabilitation
Finnish Association for Mental Health
Niemikoti Foundation
STAKES, the national research and development centre for health and welfare

Organisations

During the course of the project, the SEU met with a range of organisations with an interest in mental health issues. We are grateful for their help with this report.

Arts Council
Association of British Insurers
Association of Chief Police Officers
Association of Directors of Social Services
British Association of Counsellors and Psychotherapists
British Association of Social Workers
British Psychological Society
Carers UK
Centrex
Chartered Institute of Housing
Circles of Friends
Citizens Advice Bureau
College of Occupational Therapists
Combat Stress
Commission for Patient and Public Involvement in Health
Counsellors and Psychotherapists in Primary Care
Disability Alliance
Disability Rights Commission
Drugscope
Employers' Forum on Disability
Experts by Experience (NIMHE)
Health and Safety Executive
Health Development Agency
Institute of Education
Institute of Psychiatry
King's Fund
Learning and Skills Council
Leonard Cheshire
Local Government Association
Lookahead Housing and Care
Loonscape
Lloyds Pharmacy
Maca
Mellow (North London)
Mencap
Mentality
Mental Health Commission, New Zealand
Mental Health Foundation
Mental Health Foundation, New Zealand
Mental Health Media
Mind
National Association for the Care and Resettlement of Offenders
National Centre for Volunteering
National Children's Bureau
NHS Confederation
National Institute of Adult Continuing Education
National Institute for Clinical Excellence
National Network of Arts in Health
National Treatment Agency
NCH

Ofcom
PACE
Pharmaceutical Services
Primhe
Relate
Rethink
Revolving Doors
Richmond Fellowship
Royal College of GPs
Royal College of Nursing
Royal College of Psychiatrists
Sainsbury Centre for Mental Health
The Samaritans
SANE
Scottish Association for Mental Health
Social Firms UK
Social Care Institute for Excellence
Stonham Housing Association
Tomorrow's People
Trident Housing Association
TUC
Turning Point
University of Newcastle
Young Minds
Zito Trust

SEU Seminars

The Social Exclusion Unit also held a number of informal seminars on a range of issues around mental health, and invited experts to discuss their opinions and experiences. We are grateful for the time and help they gave us.

Employment	Bob Grove, Sainsbury Centre for Mental Health
Ethnicity	Patrick Vernon, Department of Health Inequalities Unit and Mind Sandra Griffiths, Mellow Paul Grey, Antenna James Nazroo, Researcher
Perspective of people with mental health problems	Rachel Perkins, South West London and St George's MH Trust Emma Harding, South West London and St George's MH Trust Two groups of people with mental health problems from London and Leeds met the SEU to give comments on the project's emerging findings
Social networks	Rachel Forrester-Jones, University of Kent Linda Seymour, Mentality Julian Leff, TAPS project
Acute mental health problems and acute care	Paul Rooney, South Birmingham Mental Health Trust Marva Clarke, Ward Sister Barbara Crosland, West Midlands Regional Development Centre
Education	Jeremy Braund, Adult Learning College, Lancaster
Benefits	Judy Scott, Consultant on benefits, mental health and employment Jeremy Coutinho, South West London and St George's MH Trust
Employers	Fred Bowen, Bury Employment, Support and Training Huw Davies, Bury Employment, Support and Training Elizabeth Gyngell, Health and Safety Executive Dee Hanlon, Employers' Forum on Disability Anthony Langan, The Samaritans Paul Lichfield, BT Steve Mason, Greater Manchester Police Karen Oliver, South West London and St George's MH Trust Stephen Peckitt, Health and Safety Executive Anne Price, Marks and Spencer Chris Sheehan, Unified Dyes Ltd Martin Stein, Local Government Employers' Organisation

The Social Exclusion Unit is also grateful to Jed Boardman (Institute of Psychiatry) and Peter Bates (National Development Team) for their assistance throughout the project.

Annex F: References

1. Office for National Statistics, *Labour Force Survey (LFS)*, August 2003, figures for England only. The LFS provides employment data on people with the following health conditions: problems with the arms or hands; legs or feet; back or neck; difficulty in seeing; difficulty in hearing; speech impediment; skin conditions or allergies; chest or breathing problems; heart/blood pressure/circulation disorders; stomach/liver/kidney/digestion problems; diabetes; depression or bad nerves; epilepsy; learning difficulties; mental illness, phobia or panics; progressive illnesses; and other problems or disabilities.
2. The Sainsbury Centre for Mental Health, *Policy Paper 3: The economic and social costs of mental illness*, (London, The Sainsbury Centre for Mental Health, 2003).
3. Department of Health, *Safety First: Five year report of the national confidential inquiry into suicide and homicide by people with mental illness*, (London, Department of Health, 2001a).
4. N Singleton, R Bumpstead, M O'Brien, A Lee and H Meltzer, *Psychiatric Morbidity Among Adults Living in Private Households, 2000,* (London, The Stationery Office, 2001).
5. *Ibid.*
6. G Thornicroft, 'Social deprivation and rates of treated mental disorder. Developing statistical models to predict psychiatric service utilisation', *The British Journal of Psychiatry,* 158 (1991): 475-484.
7. R Jenkins, A McCulloch, L Friedli and C Parker, *Developing a National Mental Health Policy,* Maudesley Monograph 43, (Hove, The Psychology Press, 2002).
8. Department of Health Prescription Cost Analysis System.
9. Incapacity Benefit admin data, August 2003, England only.
10. The number of people claiming Jobseekers' Allowance in the UK stood at 876,300 in April 2004. Office for National Statistics, *Labour Market Statistics,* May 2004, (London, Office for National Statistics, 2004).
11. R Crowther, M Marshall, GR Bond and P Huxley, 'Vocational rehabilitation for people with severe mental illness' (Cochrane Review), *The Cochrane Library*, Issue 1 (2004).
12. N Singleton, NA Maung, A Cowie, J Sparks, R Bumpstead and H Meltzer, *Mental Health of Carers,* (London, Office for National Statistics, The Stationery Office, 2002).
13. J Aldridge and S Becker, *Children caring for parents with mental illness: perspectives of young carers, parents and professional,* (Bristol, The Policy Press, 2003).
14. Taylor Nelson Sofres, *Attitudes to Mental Illness 2003 Report*, (London, Department of Health/Office for National Statistics, 2003).
15. C Manning and PD White, 'Attitudes of employers to the mentally ill', *Psychiatric Bulletin*, 19 (1995): 541-543.
16. Financial mapping returns collated by Mental Health Strategies (2003) (unpublished).
17. Office for National Statistics, *Labour Force Survey: Household datasets*, spring quarter 2003.
18. J Morris, *The right support: report of the task force on supporting disabled adults in their parenting role,* (York, Joseph Rowntree Foundation, 2003).
19. J Rankin and S Regan, *Meeting Complex Needs: The Future of Social Care,* (London, ippr/Turning Point, 2004).
20. Social Exclusion Unit, *Tackling Social Exclusion: Taking Stock and Looking to the Future (Emerging Findings)*, (London, Office of the Deputy Prime Minister, 2004).
21. Figures based on the ILO unemployment rate. Office for National Statistics, *Labour Market Statistics, May 2004*, (London, Office for National Statistics, 2004).
22. Department for Work and Pensions, *Opportunity for all: 5th Annual Report,* (London, Department for Work and Pensions, 2003).
23. Department for Education and Skills, *Every Child Matters*, (London, Department for Education and Skills, 2003).
24. Office of the Deputy Prime Minister, *Rough Sleeping Estimates in England*, accessed at: http://www.odpm.gov.uk/stellent/groups/odpm_homelessness/documents/page/odpm_home_024898.hcsp.
25. EC Harris and B Barraclough, 'Excess Mortality of mental disorders', *British Journal of Psychiatry*, 173 (1998): 11-53.
26. Mentality, *Promoting Healthy Living for People with mental health problems,* (London, Mentality, 2003); P Allebeck, 'Schizophrenia: A Life-Shortening Disease', *Psychiatric Bulletin*, 15 (1) (1989):81-89.
27. The Sainsbury Centre for Mental Health, *op. cit.,* 2003.

28. N Singleton *et al, op. cit.,* 2001. All findings presented from this source relate to adults aged 16-74 living in Great Britain unless otherwise stated. This figure underestimates prevalence as it only reflects those living in private households, not those living in institutions or who are homeless. For example, the Office of Population Census and Surveys (OPCS) survey of psychiatric morbidity in institutions (H Meltzer, B Gill, M Petticrew and K Hinds, *The prevalence of psychiatric morbidity among adults living in institutions* (London, The Stationery Office, 1996) estimated that 70 per cent of the 33,200 people living in institutions (hospital and residential care) catering for people with mental illness suffered from schizophrenia, delusional and schizo-affective disorders; 8 per cent of individuals suffered from stress-related or somatoform disorders and 8 per cent from affective disorders. Further, people with a severe mental illness are also less likely to respond to general surveys. Thus, estimates for the number of people with severe and enduring mental health problems have varied from 0.3-1.5 per cent of the adult population (L Bird, *Fundamental Facts*, (London, Mental Health Foundation, 1999).

29. Although the 2000 Psychiatric Morbidity Survey estimated the prevalence of 'neurotic disorders' at 164 per 1,000 population, further analysis of the survey data to include those aged between 16-64 living in England only indicated a slightly higher rate of 175 per 1,000 population. Estimates are based on respondents experiencing symptoms of certain 'neurotic disorders' during the week before interview.

30. Office for National Statistics, *Labour Force Survey (LFS)*, August 2003, figures for England only. Within the definition of the LFS, those 'in work' includes all people who are aged 16 and over who did some paid work in the reference week (whether as employed or self-employed); those who had a job they were temporarily away from (on holiday for example); those on government-supported training and employment programmes; and those doing unpaid family work. The definition of 'disabled' is in line with the definition used within the Disability Discrimination Act 1996 as detailed in Chapter 3 which includes people with a mental impairment that has a substantial and long-term adverse effect on their ability to carry out day-to-day activities.

31. T Burchadt, *Employment retention and the onset of sickness or disability: Evidence from the Labour Force Survey longitudinal datasets*, Department for Work and Pensions in-house report no. 109, (2003).

32. J Kim-Cohen, 'Prior Juvenile Diagnoses in Adults with Mental Disorder', *Archives of General Psychiatry*, 60 (7) (2003): 709-717.

33. Department of Health, *op. cit.,* 2001a.

34. H Meltzer, N Singleton, A Lee, P Bebbington, T Brugha and R Jenkins, *The Social and Economic Circumstances of Adults with Mental Disorders*, (London, The Stationery Office, 2002).

35. Shelter, *House Keeping: Preventing homelessness through tackling rent arrears in social housing,* (London, Shelter, 2003).

36. H Meltzer *et al, op. cit.,* 2002.

37. The Sainsbury Centre for Mental Health, *op. cit.,* 2003.

38. *Ibid.* The researchers do not include this figure within the overall costs of £77.4 billion. Benefit payments are interpreted as a transfer of resources rather than a strict economic cost.

39. Department of Health statistical bulletin, *Prescriptions dispensed in the community: England 1992-2002,* accessed at: http://www.publications.doh.gov.uk/public/sb0312.htm.

40. H Meltzer *et al, op. cit.,* 2002.

41. N Singleton *et al, op. cit.,* 2001. As previously indicated, this survey relates only to those living in private households and is therefore highly likely to underestimate prevalence in the entire population.

42. The Office for National Statistics Psychiatric Morbidity Survey (N Singleton *et al, op. cit.,* 2001) has adopted the American Psychiatric Association (1994) definition of personality disorder. This defines personality disorder as 'an enduring pattern of inner experience and behaviour that deviates markedly from the expectation of the individual's culture, is pervasive and inflexible, has an onset in adolescence or early adulthood, is stable over time, and leads to distress or impairment'.

43. L Bird, *Fundamental Facts*, (London, Mental Health Foundation, 1999).

44. N Singleton *et al, op. cit.,* 2001. Due to the fluctuating nature of mental health problems, during the course of a year, the rates of common mental health problems will be higher than in any one week. Thus, Goldberg and Huxley (D Goldberg and P Huxley, *Common mental disorders: A bio social model,* (London, Tavistock/Routledge, 1992) estimated that as many as one in four people will develop a common mental disorder during the course of a year and Andrews (G Andrews, 'Meeting the unmet need for disease management', in G Andrews and S Henderson (eds.), *Unmet Need in Psychiatry: Problems, Resources, Responses,* (Cambridge, Cambridge University Press, 2000)) has suggested that the one year prevalence may be around a third higher at 24 per cent.

45. Mental Health Foundation website, http://www.mentalhealth.org.uk/page.cfm?pagecode=PMNZPN.

46. The 2000 Psychiatric Morbidity Survey is a repeat of a survey carried out in 1993. There was no significant change in the overall rates for common and more severe mental health problems at these two time points. However, there was a slight but significant increase in the prevalence of neurotic disorder among men (from 126 per 1,000 in 1993 to 144 per 1,000 in 2000).

47. World Health Organisation, *The World Health Report 2001. Mental Health: New Understanding, New Hope,* (Geneva, World Health Organisation, 2001).

48. M Rutter and DJ Smith (eds.) *Psychosocial disorders in young people: time trends and their causes,* (New York, John Wiley, 1995).

49. Since April 2001, no new claims for Severe Disablement Allowance have been allowed. However, people who were claiming SDA before this date can still receive it provided that they continue to meet the eligibility criteria.

50. Incapacity Benefit admin data, August 2003, England only. In August 2003, 848,800 people were claiming Incapacity Benefit and 58,200 were claiming Severe Disablement Allowance because of mental health problems – a total of 907,000 people.

51. According to evidence gathered as part of the Social Exclusion Unit project.

52. BJ Burchell, D Day, M Hudson, D Ladipo, R Mankelow, JP Nolan, H Reed, IC Wichert and F Wilkinson (ESRC Centre for Business Research at Cambridge University), *Job insecurity and work intensification: Flexibility and the changing boundaries of work,* (York, Joseph Rowntree Foundation, 1999).

53. Based on a follow-up of the people interviewed in the 2000 Psychiatric Morbidity survey: N Singleton and G Lewis, *Better or Worse: a longitudinal study of the mental health of adults living in private households in Great Britain,* (London, The Stationery Office, 2003).

54. Department of Health, *op. cit.,* 2001a.

55. L Bird, *op. cit.*, 1999. Men are likely to have an earlier onset, poorer outcomes and longer-term service use.

56. N Singleton *et al, op. cit.,* 2001.

57. D Melzer, T Fryers and R Jenkins (eds.) *Social Inequalities and the Distribution of the Common Mental Disorders, Maudsley Monograph 44,* (Hove, Psychology Press, 2004). In this analysis, among those assessed as having a 'neurotic disorder', the disorder was defined as 'limiting' where the person's symptoms had stopped them from getting on with things they used to do or would like to do. The disorder was defined as 'disabling' if a person had a limiting disorder and also had at least one difficulty with an activity of daily living.

58. D Melzer *et al, op. cit.,* 2004.

59. *Ibid.*

60. Department of Health, *The Mental Health Policy Implementation Guide,* (London, Department of Health, 2001b).

61. J Kim-Cohen, *op. cit.,* 2003.

62. N Singleton *et al, op. cit.,* 2001.

63. The Office for National Statistics Psychiatric Morbidity Survey (N Singleton *et al, op. cit.,* 2001) estimated rates of 19 per cent of women and 14 per cent of men as having neurotic disorders, rates of 5 per 1,000 population for women and 6 per 1,000 population for men for psychotic disorders and rates of 54 per 1,000 men and 34 per 1,000 women for personality disorders.

64. Department of Health, *Our Healthier Nation: A contract for health – a consultation paper,* (London, The Stationery Office, 1998).

65. B Audini and P Lelliott, 'Age, gender and ethnicity of those detained under Part II of the Mental Health Act 1983', *British Journal of Psychiatry,* 180 (2003): 222-226.

66. K Spronston and J Nazroo, *Ethnic Minority Psychiatric Illness Rates in the Community (EMPIRIC) – Quantitative Report,* (London, The Stationery Office, 2002).

67. L Bird, *op. cit.,* 1999.

68. VS Raleigh and R Balarajan, 'Suicide levels and trends among immigrants in England and Wales', *Health Trends,* 24 (1992): 91-94; VS Raleigh, 'Suicide patterns and trends in people of Indian subcontinent and Caribbean origin in England and Wales', *Ethnicity and Health,* 1 (1) (1996): 55-63.

69. K Spronston and J Nazroo, *op. cit.,* 2002.

70. D Melzer *et al, op. cit.,* 2002.

71. L Platt, *Parallel Lives? Poverty among ethnic minority groups in Britain,* (London, Child Poverty Action Group, 2002).

72. D Melzer *et al, op. cit.,* 2002.

73. J Maher and H Green, *General Household Survey – Carers 2000,* (London, Office for National Statistics, 2000). The category of 'mental disability' is likely to include people with a learning disability and people with both functional and organic mental health problems.

74. J Aldridge and S Becker, *op. cit.*, 2003.

75. N Singleton *et al, op. cit.,* 2002.

76. Mentality website, http://www.mentality.org.uk/services/promotion/prevalence.htm

77. A Smith, C Brice, A Collins, V Matthews and R McNamara, *The scale of occupational stress: A further analysis of the impact of demographic factors and type of job. Contract Research report 311/2000,* (Suffolk, Health & Safety Executive, 2000).

78. Samaritans, *Information Resource Pack 2003*, (2003), accessed at: http://www.samaritans.org/know/pdf/InfoResourcePack2003web.pdf

79. Patient UK website, Patient Information Publications, Post Traumatic Stress Disorder (PTSD), accessed at: http://www.patient.co.uk/showdoc.asp?doc=27000223.

80. A Braidwood (ed.), *Psychological Injury, Understanding and Supporting Proceedings of DSS War Pensions Agency Conference, London,* (London, The Stationery Office, 2000).

81. Office for National Statistics, *Geographic Variations in Health,* (Office for National Statistics, The Stationery Office, 2001).

82. D Melzer *et al, op. cit.,* 2002.

83. KA Kendall-Tackett, LM Williams and D Finkelhor, 'Impact of Sexual Abuse of Children: A Review and Synthesis of Recent Empirical Studies', *Psychological Bulletin,* 113 (1993): 164-180.

84. B Iddon, Chairman of All Party Parliamentary Drugs Misuse Group, in *Hansard*, part 2 July 1999 Column 567.

85. Turning Point, *Waiting for Change: Treatment delays and the damage to drinkers,* (London, Turning Point, 2003).

86. T Weaver, V Charles, P Madden and A Renton, *Co-morbidity of Substance Misuse and Mental Illness collaborative study (COSMIC),* Research report submitted to the Department of Health September 2002.

87. Social Exclusion Unit, *Reducing re-offending by ex-prisoners*, (London, Social Exclusion Unit, 2003).

88. N Singleton, H Meltzer, R Gatward, J Coid and D Deasy, *Psychiatric Morbidity among Prisoners in England and Wales*, (Office for National Statistics, The Stationery office, 1998). The prevalence rates for any functional psychosis in the past year were 7 per cent for male sentenced, 10 per cent for male remand and 14 per cent for female prisoners. Schizophrenic or delusional disorders were more common than affective disorders. This compares to the rate of four per thousand (0.4 per cent) in the general household population.

89. *Ibid.*

90. HM Prison Service, *Annual Report and Accounts April 2002 – March 2003*, July 2003.

91. Mental Health Foundation, *Fundamental Facts: Suicide And Deliberate Self-Harm*, Briefing No. 1. (London, Mental Health Foundation, 1997).

92. S Griffiths, *Addressing the Health Needs of Rough Sleepers,* (London, Office of the Deputy Prime Minister, 2002).

93. B Gill, H Meltzer, K Hinds and Mark Petticrew. *Psychiatric morbidity among homeless people*, (London, The Stationery Office, 1996). This survey found that an estimated that 60 per cent of people staying in night shelters and 57 per cent of people sleeping rough using day centres had symptoms indicative of common mental health problems and that almost a half (43 per cent and 47 per cent respectively) were positive on at least one of the psychosis sift criteria.

94 A Burnett and M Peel, 'Health Needs of Asylum Seekers and Refugees', *British Medical Journal,* 322 (2001): 544-547.

95. BL Nicholson, 'The influence of pre-migration and post-emigration stressors on mental health: a study of southeast Asian refugees', *Social Work Research*, 21 (1) (1997):19-32.

96. N Patel and I Fatimilehin, 'Racism and mental health', in G Newnes, G Holmes, C Dunn, (eds.), *This is madness: a critical look at psychiatry and the future of Mental Health Services,* (Ross on Wye, PCCS, 1999).

97. E Cantor Graae and JP Selten, 'Schizophrenia and Migration: A Meta-Analysis', *Schizophrenia Research*, 67 (1) (2004): 63.

98. The Foundation for People with Learning Disabilities. *Statistics on Learning Disabilities, 2003*, accessed at: http://www.learningdisabilities.org.uk/page.cfm?pagecode=ISST. The higher rates of mental health problems may be because of difficulty in communication, increased stress or general ill health.

99. PA Hindley and N Kitson (eds.), *Mental Health and Deafness*, (London, Whurr Publications, 2000).

100. Department of Health statistics: Registered Blind and Partially Sighted People, Year ending 31 March 2000, accessed at: http://www.doh.gov.uk/public/blindandpartiallysighted.htm.

101. J Repper and R Perkins, *Social inclusion and recovery: a model for medical practice*, (London, Baillière Tindall, 2003).

102. This is in line with the social model of disability, which recognises that a medically-based approach does not adequately cover the degree of exclusion faced by many people with mental health problems. Instead, the model emphasises that in reality, much of the disadvantage experienced is a function of the attitudes and structures prevalent in wider society.

103. Quoted on Mind website, accessed at: http://www.mind.org.uk/About+Mind/Jobs/

104. BG Link, EL Struening, M Rahav, JC Phelan and L Nuttbrock, 'On Stigma and its Consequences, Evidence from a Longitudinal Study of Men with Dual Diagnoses of Mental Illness and Substance Abuse.' *Journal of Health and Social Behaviour,* 38 (1997): 177-190.

105. L Sayce, 'Beyond Good Intentions: Making Anti-Discrimination Strategies Work, *Disability and Society,* 18(5) (2003): 625-642.

106. Taylor Nelson Sofres, *op. cit.,* 2003.

107. Quoted in L Sayce, *From Psychiatric Patient to Citizen, Overcoming Discrimination and Social Exclusion,* (Basingstoke, Palgrave, 2000).

108. G Green, C Hayes, D Dickinson, B Gilheany and A Whittaker, 'A mental health service users' perspective to stigmatisation', *Journal of Mental Health,* 12 (3) (2003): 223-234; BG Link, *Evidence concerning the consequences of stigma for the self-esteem of people with severe mental illnesses*, conference paper cited in M Knight, T Wykes, P Hayward, 'People don't understand': An investigation of stigma in schizophrenia using Interpretative Phenomenological Analysis (IPA)', *Journal of Mental Health*, 12 (3) (2003): 209-222.

109. Mind, *Not Alone? Isolation and mental distress,* (London, Mind, 2004).

110. L Main, 'Scare in the Community', *Mental Health Today,* July/August 2003.

111. Department of Health, *op. cit.,* 2001a.

112. P Taylor and J Gunn, 'Homicides by people with mental illness', *British Journal of Psychiatry*, 174 (1999): 9-14.

113. E Walsh, P Moran, C Scott, K McKenzie, T Burns, F Creed, P Tyrer, RM Murray and T Fahy, 'Prevalence of violent victimisation in severe mental illness', *British Journal of Psychiatry,* 183 (3) (2003): 233 – 238.

114. GR Bond, DR Becker, RE Drake, CA Rapp, N Meisler, AF Lehman and MD Bell, 'Implementing supported employment as an evidence-based practice', *Psychiatric Services,* 52 (3) (2001): 313-322.

115. R Crowther *et al*, *op. cit.,* 2004.

116. Office for National Statistics, *Labour Force Survey,* spring data set 2003, figures for England only.

117. N Singleton *et al*, *op.cit.,* 2001.

118. Quoted in Mind, *Counting the Cost*: *Mental Health in the Media*, (London, Mind, 2000).

119. D Crepaz-Keay, 'A sense of perspective: The Media and the Boyd Inquiry', in G Philo (ed.), *Media and Mental Distress,* (Harlow, Addison Wesley Longman Ltd, 1996).

120. Health Education Authority, *Discrimination Hurts,* press release, 5th October 1998.

121. G Ward, *Making Headlines*: *Mental Health and the National Press,* (London, Health Education Authority, 1997).

122. AH Crisp, MG Gelder, S Rix, HI Meltzer and OJ Rowlands, 'Stigmatisation of people with mental illnesses', *British Journal of Psychiatry*, 177 (2000): 4-7.

123. DH Granello, P Pauley and A Carmichael, 'The relationship of the media to attitudes toward people with mental illness', *Journal of Humanistic Counseling, Education and Development,* 38 (1999): 98-110.

124. C Wilson, R Nairn, J Coverdale and A Panapa, 'How mental illness is portrayed in children's television', *British Journal of Psychiatry,* 176 (2000): 440-443.

125. Mind, *op. cit.*, 2000.

126. Quoted in MTD Knight, T Wykes and P Hayward, 'People don't understand': An investigation of stigma in schizophrenia using Interpretive Phenomenological Analysis', *Journal of Mental Health*, 12 (3) (2003): 209-222.

127. Quoted in L Warner, *Out at Work*: *A Survey of the Experiences of People with Mental Health Problems within the Workplace,* (London, Mental Health Foundation, 2002).

128. C Manning and PD White, *op. cit.,* 1995.

129. S Roberts, C Heaver, K Hill, J Rennison, B Stafford, N Howat, G Kelly, S Krishnan, P Tapp and A Thomas, *Disability in the workplace: Employers and service providers' response to the Disability Discrimination Act in 2003 and preparation for 2004 changes. Department for Work and Pensions, Research report 202,* (Leeds, Corporate Document Services, 2004).

130. N Glozier, 'The workplace effects of the stigmatisation of depression', *Journal of Occupational and Environmental Medicine*, 40 (1998): 783-800.

131. J Read and S Baker, *Not just sticks and stones: A survey of the discrimination experienced by people with mental health problems*, (London, Mind, 1996).

132. J Read and S Baker, *op. cit.,* 1996.

133. Mindout for mental health, *Working minds: making mental health your business,* (London, Mind, 2000).

134. J Read and S Baker, *op. cit.,* 1996.

135. V Pinfold, P Byrne and H Toulmin, 'Challenging stigma and discrimination in communities: A focus group study identifying UK mental health service users' main campaign priorities', submitted for forthcoming publication in the *International Journal of Social Psychiatry,* (November 2003).

136. Mental Health Foundation, *Pull Yourself Together! A survey of the stigma and discrimination faced by people who experience mental distress,* (London, The Mental Health Foundation, 2000).

137. Quoted in D Rose, *Living in the Community,* (London, The Sainsbury Centre for Mental Health, 1996).

138. J Read and S Baker, *op. cit.,* 1996.

139. G Green *et al, op. cit.,* 2003.

140. The Sainsbury Centre for Mental Health, *Breaking the Circles of Fear,* (London, The Sainsbury Centre for Mental Health, 2002a).

141. S Parsons and J Dowd, *An Evaluation Of the pilot Mental Health Awareness Training carried out by Northumbria Police,* (Newcastle, Forensic Psychiatry and Clinical Psychology Research Group, Faculty of Medical Sciences, University of Newcastle, 2004).

142. TA Fahy and J Dunn, 'Where Section 136 Fails', *Police Review,* 95 (1987):1580-1.

143. J Walker, *Police Contact with the Mentally Disordered,* (London, Police Research Group, 2002).

144. J Read and S Baker, *op. cit.,* 1996.

145. Taylor Nelson Sofres, *op. cit.,* 2003.

146. J Read and S Baker, *op. cit.,* 1996.

147. V Pinfold, H Toulmin, G Thornicroft, P Huxley, P Farmer and T Graham, 'Reducing psychiatric stigma and discrimination: evaluation of educational interventions in UK secondary schools', *British Journal of Psychiatry,* 182 (2003): 342-6.

148. E Gale, L Seymour, D Crepaz-Keay, M Gibbons, P Farmer, V Pinfold, *Scoping review on Mental Health Anti-Stigma and Discrimination – Current activities and what works,* (Leeds, NIMHE, 2004).

149. *Ibid.*

150. This is campaign cost only. Including implementation budget this equates to 160 pence.

151. Funding is as follows: £485,000 in 2002-03, £850,000 in 2003-04, £800,000 planned for 2004-05, and £850,000 planned for 2005-06. Funds are provided from the Scottish Executive's National Programme for Improving Mental Health and Well-Being. The Programme's funds are part of the Executive's Health Improvement Funds from 2003-06.

152. LA Alexander and BG Link, 'The impact of contact on stigmatizing attitudes toward people with mental illness', *Journal of Mental Health,* 12 (3) (2003): 271-289.

153. E Gale *et al, op. cit.,* 2004.

154. Office for National Statistics, *Labour Force Survey*, autumn 2003.

155. Disability Rights Commission response to Social Exclusion Unit consultation.

156. S Leverton, *Monitoring the Disability Discrimination Act 1992 (Phase 2),* Department for Work and Pensions In-House Report, Series No 91 (2002).

157. The Sainsbury Centre for Mental Health, *An executive briefing on primary care mental health services,* Briefing 19, (London, The Sainsbury Centre for Mental Health, 2002b).

158. R Jenkins *et al, op. cit.,* 2002.

159. Maca, *First National GP Survey of Mental Health in Primary Care,* (London, Maca, 1999).

160. Norwich Union Healthcare, *Health of the Nation Report,* (Norwich, 2004). Norwich Union Healthcare has commissioned Dr Foster to conduct ongoing research with a panel of 255 GPs on a range of issues. Reports are published twice a year or accessed at: http://www.norwichunion.com/health/publicrelations/health_nation.htm

161. Department of Health Prescription Cost Analysis System.

162. Department of Health, *A Responsive and High Quality Local NHS: The Primary Care Progress Report 2004,* (London, Department of Health, 2004a).

163. N Aylward and K James, *Prescriptions for Learning Project Nottingham 2nd Evaluation Report,* (Place, National Institute for Adult Continuing Education/Nottingham Health Action Zone December 2002).

164. *Ibid.*

165. A Killoran, P Fentem and C Caspersen (eds), *Moving On: International Perspectives on Promoting Physical Activity,* (London, Health Education Authority, 1994), quoted in S Collinson and C Manning, *Resource Pack: Promoting Mental Health, Cultivating Social Inclusion & Managing Mental Health Problems in Primary Care,* (Primhe, 2003).

166. D Browne, 'Exercise Prescription', *Royal Society of Health,* 117 (1) (1997): 52-55.

167. PJ Huxley, *Arts on Prescription: an evaluation,* (Stockport, Stockport NHS Trust, 1997).

168. J Simons, J Reynolds and L Morison, 'Randomised controlled trial of training health visitors to identify and help couples with relationship problems following a birth.' *British Journal of General Practice,* vol. no. 51 (471)(2001): 793-799.

169. J Shearn, *Student Counselling Service Annual Report, 2002-2003,* (Cardiff, Cardiff University, 2003) accessed at: http://www.cf.ac.uk/ssd/counselling/annrep2003.html

170. D Bhugra and V Bhal (eds.), *Ethnicity : An agenda for mental health,* (London, Gaskell, 1999).

171. Department of Health, *Organising and Delivering Psychological Therapies,* (London, Department of Health, 2004b). Also available from www.dh.gov.uk/mentalhealth and www.nimhe.org.uk

172. EC Harris and B Barraclough, *op. cit.* 1998.

173. Mentality, *op. cit.,* 2003; P Allebeck, *op. cit.,* 1989.

174. O Evans, N Singleton, H Meltzer, R Stewart and M Prince, *The mental health of older people,* (London, Office for National Statistics, 2003).

175. M Phelan, L Stradins and S Morrison, 'Physical health of people with severe mental illness', *British Medical Journal,* 322 (2001): 443-444.

176. R McCreadie and C Kelly, 'Patients with schizophrenia who smoke: private disaster, public resource', Editorial, *British Journal of Psychiatry,* 176 (2002): 109.

177. Institute of Alcohol Studies, *Factsheet: Alcohol and Mental Health,* (St Ives (Cambridgeshire), Institute of Alcohol Studies, 2003).

178. A McNeill, *Smoking and Mental Health – A Review of the Literature,* (London, Smoke Free London Programme, 2001).

179. M Coultard, M Farrell M, N Singleton and H Meltzer, *Tobacco, Alcohol and Drug Use and mental health,* (London, The Stationery Office, 2000).

180. EC Harris and C Barraclough, *op. cit.,* 1998.

181. Mentality, *An Executive Briefing on mental health promotion: implementing Standard One of the National Service Framework,* (London, Mentality, 2001).

182. Mentality, *op. cit.,* 2003.

183. Department of Health, *Tackling Health Inequalities: A programme for action,* (London, Department of Health, 2003a).

184. Mental Health Strategies, *A Modern Guide to Primary Care Mental Health Services,* accessed at: http://www.mentalhealthstrategies.co.uk/pdf_files/Modern%20Guide.pdf

185. Department of Health, *Mental Health Policy Implementation Guide: Adult acute inpatient care provision,* (London, Department of Health, 2002).

186. The Care Programme Approach was introduced by joint Health and Social Services circular, HC(90)23/LASSL(90)11, (London, Department of Health, 1990).

187. Department of Health, *Effective Care Co-ordination of Mental Health Services: Modernising the Care Programme Approach, A Policy Booklet,* (London, Department of Health, 1999a).

188. For example, Commission for Health Improvement, *Emerging Themes from mental health trust Reviews,* (London, Commission for Health Improvement, 2003).

189. This includes use of self-assessment, recovery, essential lifestyle or person-centred planning approaches.

190. M Marshall and A Lockwood, 'ACT for people with severe mental disorders' (Cochrane review), *The Cochrane library*, Issue 3 (1998).

191. Financial mapping returns collated by Mental Health Strategies (2003) (unpublished).

192. Community Care (Direct Payments) Act (1996). Certain people whose liberty to arrange their care is restricted by mental health or criminal justice legislation are excluded from having a direct payment (see The Community Care, Services for Carers and Children's Services (Direct Payments) (England) Regulations 2003, Statutory Instrument 2003 No. 762). However, the vast majority of people with mental health problems are not subject to this legislation, and are therefore potentially eligible for direct payments.

193. Although direct payments were originally introduced for disabled adults, access to direct payments has been extended more recently to other groups including carers (Health and Social Care Act 2001, Carers and Disabled Children Act 2000).

194. This year, the Department of Health will launch a public consultation about renaming 'direct payments' as the same term is used by the Department for Work and Pensions in relation to the paying welfare benefits directly into beneficiaries' bank accounts.

195. D Robbins, *Treated as People. An overview of mental health services from a social care perspective, 2002-2004,* (London, Social Services Inspectorate/Department of Health, 2004)

196. Figures from the Social Services Inspectorate Performance Assessment: Delivery and Improvement Analysis indicate that at the end of September 2003, 10,616 adults in contact with Social Services Departments (excluding carers) were using direct payments. Of these, the majority (67 per cent) were people with a physical disability (including people with a sensory impairment), with relatively lower numbers of older people (18 per cent), people with a learning disability (13 per cent) and people with mental health problems (2 per cent) in receipt of direct payments.

197. H Spandler and N Vick, *Direct payments, independent living and mental health,* (London, Health and Social Care Advisory Service, 2004)

198. H Spandler and N Vick, *op. cit.*, 2004; S Witcher, K Stalker, M Roadburg and C Jones *Direct Payments: The Impact on Choice and Control for Disabled People,* (Edinburgh, Scottish Human Services Trust and Lothian Centre for Integrated Living, The Scottish Executive Central Research Unit, 2000); J Ridley and L Jones *'Direct what?': A study of direct payments to mental health service users* (Edinburgh, Scottish Executive Central Research Unit, 2002); RA Maglajlic, 'The Silent Treatment' *OpenMind*, 99: 12-13.

199. Maca, *op. cit.,* 1999.

200. The Sainsbury Centre for Mental Health, *op. cit.,* 2002.

201. Disability Alliance, *Disability Rights Handbook*, (London, Disability Alliance Educational & Research Association, 2001); A McHarron and M Nettle, *Payment to service users. Guidance paper,* (Birmingham, West Midlands partnership for Mental Health,1999); J Scott and P Seebohm , *Payments and the Benefits System: A guide for survivors and service users involved in improving mental health services,* (London, Institute for Applied Health & Social Policy, King's College London, 2001); J Scott and P Seebohm, *Payments and the Benefits System: A guide for managers paying survivors and service users involved in improving mental health services,* (London, Institute for Applied Health & Social Policy, King's College London, 2001).

202. Allies in Change, *User and carer participation route map,* (Edinburgh, Scottish Development Centre for Mental Health, 2001); S Foster and A McHarron, *Involving Users and Carers in Policy Implementation,* (Birmingham, West Midlands partnership for Mental Health, 2001,); North West Mental Health Development Centre, *Good Practice Guidelines for Involving Service Users and Carers in Local Implementation Teams,* (Manchester, North West Mental Health Development Centre, 2001).

203. T Ryan and C Bamber , 'A survey of policy and practice on expenses and other payments to mental health service users and carers participating in service development', *Journal of Mental Health,* 11 (6) (2002): 635-644.

204. L Sayce, *op cit.,* 2003.

205. Norfolk, Suffolk and Cambridgeshire Strategic Health Authority, *Independent Inquiry into the death of David Bennett,* (Cambridge, Norfolk, Suffolk and Cambridgeshire Strategic Health Authority, 2003).

206. G Sandamas and G Hogman, *No Change?,* (London, National Schizophrenia Fellowship (now Rethink), 2000).

207. National Institute for Mental Health in England, *Inside Outside: Improving Mental Health Services for Black and Minority Ethnic Communities in England,* (Leeds, Department of Health, 2003).

208. G Sandamas and G Hogman, *op. cit.,* 2000.

209. J Nazroo, *Ethnicity, Class and Health,* (London, Policy Studies Institute, 2001).

210. G Glover, R Dean and C Hartley, *National Child and Adolescent Mental Health Service Mapping Exercise,* (Durham, Department of Health and University of Durham, 2003).

211. C Wilson, *Breaking Down the Barriers: Key Findings,* (London,Youth Access, 2001).

212. Department of Health, *Getting the Right Start: The National Service Framework for Children, Young People and Maternity Services – Emerging Findings,* (London, Department of Health, 2003b).

213. Audit Commission, *Forget Me Not: Mental Health Services for Older People,* (London, Audit Commission, 2000); Social Services Inspectorate, *Improving Older People's Services: Inspection of Social Care Services for Older People* (London, Social Services Inspectorate/Department of Health, 2002).

214. J Morris, *op. cit.,* 2003.

215. Countryside Agency, *Rural Services in 2000, results from the Countryside Agency's Survey,* (Cheltenham, Countryside Agency, 2001).

216. H Castillo, *Personality Disorder, Temperament or Trauma,* (London, Jessica Kingsley Publishers, 2003).

217. National Institute for Mental Health in England, *Personality disorder: No longer a diagnosis of exclusion,* (London, National Institute for Mental Health in England, 2003b).

218. *Ibid.*

219. KA Kendall-Tackett, LM Williams and D Finkelhor, 'Impact of Sexual Abuse of Children: A Review and Synthesis of Recent Empirical Studies', *Psychological Bulletin,* 113 (1993): 164-180.

220. J Richardson, J Coid, A Petruckevitch, WS Chung, S Moorey, and G Feder, 'Identifying Domestic Violence: Cross-Sectional Study in Primary Care', *British Medical Journal,* 324 (2) (2002): 274-277.

221. J Rankin and S Regan, *op. cit,* 2004.

222. *Ibid.*

223. C Pristach and C Smith, 'Medication compliance and substance abuse among schizophrenic patients', *Hospital & Community Psychiatry,* 41 (1990): 1345-1348; A Ley, DP Jeffery, S McLaren and N Siegfried, 'Treatment programmes for people with both severe mental illness and substance misuse' (Cochrane Review), *The Cochrane library,* Issue 2 (1999).

224. MS Ridgely, HH Goldman and M Willenbring, 'Barrier to the care of persons with dual diagnosis: organisational and financial issues', *Schizophrenia Bulletin,* 16(1), (1990):123–32; A Ley *et al., op. cit.,* 1999.

225. Mind, *Mental Health Problems and Learning Disability Factsheet,* accessed at: http://www.mind.org.uk/information/factsheets/learning+disabilities

226. Social Exclusion Unit, *Rough Sleeping,* (London, SEU,1998).

227. Department of Health, internal figures on waiting times from assessment to transfer, 2003.

228. Home Office, *Statistics on Race and the Criminal Justice System, 2002,* (London, Home Office, 2003).

229. Home Office, *Outcome of psychiatric admission through the courts, Research Development Statistics Occasional Paper No. 79,* (London, Home Office, 2002).

230. Figures quoted are according to the Labour Force Survey definition – see reference 30.

231. R Crowther *et al, op. cit.,* 2004.

232. 35 per cent of adults with long-term mental health problems who are economically inactive would like to work, compared to 28 per cent for other health problems. Office for National Statistics, *Labour Force Survey,* spring data set 2003, figures for England only.

233. W Anthony, A Howell and KS Danley, 'Vocational Rehabilitation of the Psychiatrically Disabled' in M Mirabi (ed.), *The Chronically Mentally Ill: Research and Services,* (Jamaica/New York, Spectrum Publications, 1984); G Shepherd, 'The Value of Work in the 1980s', *Psychiatric Bulletin,* 13 (1989): 231-233.

234. N Singleton *et al, op. cit.,* 2001.

235. C Howarth, P Kenway, G Palmer and C Street, *Monitoring poverty and social exclusion: Labour's inheritance,* (York, Joseph Rowntree Foundation, 1998).

236. MD Bell, R Milstein and PH Lysaker, 'Pay as an incentive in work participation by patients with severe mental illness'; *Hospital and Community Psychiatry,* 44 (1993): 684-686; JA Cook and L Razzano, 'Vocational rehabilitation for persons with schizophrenia: Recent research and implications for practice', *Schizophrenia Bulletin,* 26(1), (2000): 87-103.

237. R Warner, *Recovery from schizophrenia, Psychiatry and Political Economy (2nd edition),* (London, Routledge Kegan Paul, 1994).

238. RE Drake, GJ Hugo, RR Bebort, DR Becker, M Harris, GR Bond and E Quimby, 'A randomised clinical trial of supported employment for inner-city patients with severe mental disorders', *Archives of General Psychiatry,* 56(7), (1999): 627-633.

239. P Warr, *Unemployment and Mental Health,* (Oxford: Oxford University Press, 1987).

240. G Lewis and A Sloggett, 'Suicide, Deprivation and Unemployment: Record Linkage Study', *British Medical Journal*, 317, (1998):1283-1286.

241. M Bartley, 'Unemployment and Ill Health: Understanding the Relationships', *Journal of Epidemiology and Community Health*, 48, (1994):333-337.

242. British Society for Rehabilitation Medicine, *Vocational Rehabilitation: The way forward: British Society for Rehabilitation Medicine,* (London, British Society of Rehabilitation Medicine, 2001).

243. S Hussey, P Hoddinott, P Wilson, J Dowell and R Barbour, 'Sickness Certification in the United Kingdom: Qualitative Study of Views of General Practitioners in Scotland', *British Medical Journal*, 328, (2004): 88; J Hiscock and J Ritchie, *The Role of GPs in Sickness Certification*, Department for Work and Pensions research report 148 (Leeds, Department for Work and Pensions, 2001).

244. This is available from the Department for Work and Pensions website: http://www.dwp.gov.uk/medical/hottopics/pilots.asp

245. Department of Health, *Mental Health and Employment,* (London, Department of Health, 2002)

246. Financial mapping returns collated by Mental Health Strategies (2003) (unpublished).

247. R Perkins, M Rinaldi, J Hardisty, E Harding, A Taylor, S Brown, *User Employment Progress Report,* (London, South West London and St George's Mental Health NHS Trust, 2004).

248. R Perkins, E Evenson and B Davidson, *The Pathfinder User Employment Programme: Increasing Access to Employment within Mental Health Services for People who have Experienced Mental Health Problems,* (London, South West London & St George's Mental Health NHS Trust, 2000).

249. M Rinaldi, K McNeil, M Firn, M Koletsi, R Perkins and SP Singh, 'What are the benefits of evidence-based supported employment for people with first episode psychosis?', *Psychiatric Bulletin* (in press).

250. Department for Trade and Industry, *The National Minimum Wage and Therapeutic Work,* (London, Department for Trade and Industry, 2003).

251. R Crowther *et al, op. cit.,* 2004.

252. M Rinaldi *et al, op. cit.*, (in press).

253. R Crowther and M Marshall, 'Employment rehabilitation schemes for people with mental health problems in the North West region: Service characteristics and utilisation', *Journal of Mental Health,* 10 (4) (2001): 373-381.

254. C Curran, M Knapp and J Beecham, *Mental Health and Social Exclusion: Economic Aspects,* Paper prepared for the Social Exclusion Unit by Personal Social Services Research Unit, London School of Economics and University of Kent at Canterbury, (2003).

255. DR Becker, GR Bond, D McCarthy, D Thompson, H Xie, GJ McHugo and RE Drake, 'Converting day treatment centers to supported employment programs in Rhode Island', *Psychiatric Services* 52 (2001): 351-357.

256. Department for Work and Pensions, Information and Analysis directorate (Information Centre) 5 per cent sample based on 1999 inflow.

257. T Burchardt, *Employment retention and the onset of sickness or disability: Evidence from Labour Force Survey Longitudinal datasets*, Department for Work and Pensions in-house report, 109, (2003).

258. See for example, Royal College of Psychiatrists, *Employment opportunities and psychiatric disability*, (London, Royal College of Psychiatrists, 2003).

259. 37 per cent of respondents to the Social Exclusion Unit consultation identified the fear of jeopardising benefits and potential loss of income as a barrier to employment.

260. J Secker, H Membrey, B Grove and P Seebohm, 'The How and Why of Workplace Adjustments: Contextualising the Evidence', *Psychiatric Rehabilitation Journal,* 27(1) (2003):3-9.

261. Housing Benefit is reduced by 65p for every £1 earned above the earnings disregard limits and Council Tax Benefit is reduced by 20p for every £1, making 85p in total. However, this does not apply while someone is claiming Income Support (even if IS is subject to the earning disregards rule), i.e. disregards do not apply concurrently to Income Support and Housing Benefit/Council Tax Benefit.

262. Since April 2001, no new claims for Severe Disablement Allowance have been allowed. However, people who were receiving SDA before this date can continue to receive it provided that they remain eligible.

263. The number of people claiming Jobseekers' Allowance in the UK stood at 876,300 in April 2004. Office for National Statistics, *Labour Market Statistics, May 2004*, (London, Office for National Statistics, 2004).

264. H Bowers, J Secker, M Llanes and D Webb, *The Forgotten Generation: Rediscovering Midlife as a Route to Healthy Active Ageing. A report of a national evaluation of eight pilots focusing on promoting health in midlife,* (London, Older People's Programme, King's College London, 2003).
265. Performance and Innovation Unit, *Winning the Generation Game,* (London, Cabinet Office, 2000).
266. Office for National Statistics, *Labour Force Survey: Household datasets,* spring quarter 2003.
267. JC Hales, C Lessof, W Roth, M Gloyer, A Shaw, J Millar, M Barnes, P Elias, C Hasluck, A McKnight and AE Green, *Evaluation of the New Deal for Lone Parents: Early Lessons from the Phase One Prototype: Synthesis Report. DSS Research Report No 108,* (Leeds, Department of Social Security, 2000).); C Hasluck, *New Deal for Lone Parents: A Summary of Progress. Employment Service Research and Development Report ESR51,* (Sheffield, Employment Service, 2000).
268. Department for Work and Pensions, *Opportunity for All, 5th annual report,* (London, Department for Work and Pensions, 2003).
269. A Pozner, ML Hammond, J Shepherd, *Working it Out,* (Brighton, Pavilion Publishing, 1996).
270. P Seebohm, J Secker and B Grove, *Hidden Skills, Hidden Talents,* (London, Employment Support Programme, Institute for Applied Health & Social Policy, King's College London, March 2003).
271. PJ Carling and P Allott, *Partnerships in mental health Directional paper II – Beyond mental health services: Integrating resources and supports in the local community,* (Birmingham, Centre for Mental Health Policy, University of Central England, 2001).
272. See for example evaluations of the Scottish Executive's New Futures Fund: LRDP Ltd in association with the Policy Research Unit and Fairley Small Consultants, *New Futures Fund – phase one evaluation,* (Glasgow, Scottish Enterprise, 2001); *New Futures Fund – phase two interim evaluation,* (Glasgow, Scottish Enterprise, 2003); A Hirst, R Tarling, M Lefaucheux and S Rinne, *Evaluation of Lone Parents and Partners Outreach Service,* (London, Department for Work and Pensions, 2003).
273. For example 49 per cent of disadvantaged young people agreed that 'they would rather seek help from a voluntary organisation rather than a statutory agency' – only 20 per cent disagreed. The Prince's Trust, *Helping the Hardest to Reach,* (London, The Prince's Trust, 2004).
274. P Thornton, *Users views of Access to Work, A Study for the Employment Service,* (University of York, Disability Services Research Partnership, 2000).
275. Department for Work and Pensions, *Building on the New Deal: Local Solutions Meeting Individual Needs – Preliminary Paper,* (London, Department for Work and Pensions, 2004).
276. S Zadek and S Scott-Parker, *Unlocking the evidence: the new disability business case,* (London, Employers' forum on disability, 2001).
277. Quoted in Mindout for Mental Health, *Working minds – making mental health your business,* (London, Mind, 2000).
278. HM Treasury, *Review of Ill Health Retirement in the Public Sector,* (London, Parliamentary Press, 2000).
279. R Perkins *et al, op. cit.,* 2000
280. According to a large-scale quantitative survey conducted in 2002. KL MacDonald-Wilson, ES Rogers, JM Massaro, A Lyass and T Crean, 'An investigation of reasonable workplace accommodations for people with psychiatric disabilities: Quantitative findings from a multi-site study', *Community Mental Health Journal,* 38 (1) (2002):35-50.
281. National Employment Panel, *A New Deal for All: Report of the National Employment Panel's working group on New Deal 25 plus,* (London, National Employment Panel, 2004).
282. L Warner, *op. cit.,* 2002.
283. Foreword to Mindout for Mental Health, *Line manager's resource: a practical guide to managing and supporting mental health in the workplace,* (London, National Institute for Mental Health in England, 2003).
284. C Diffley, *Managing mental health: Research into the management of mental health in the workplace,* (London, The Work Foundation/Mindout, 2003).
285. Mindout for Mental Health, *op. cit.,* 2003.
286. Disability Rights Commission, *Coming Together: Mental Health Service Users and Disability Rights,* (London, Disability Rights Commission, 2003).
287. R Bodman, R Davies, N Frankel, L Minton, L Mitchell, C Pacé, R Sayers, N Tibbs, Z Tovey and E Unger, *Life's Labours Lost: A study of the experiences of people who have lost their occupation following mental health problems,* (London, Mental Health Foundation, 2003).
288. P Huxley and G Thornicroft, 'Social Inclusion, Social Quality and Mental Illness', *The British Journal of Psychiatry,* 182 (2003): 289-290.

289. H Meltzer, *Further analysis of the Psychiatric Morbidity Survey 2000*, Data prepared for the Social Exclusion Unit (2003). (Figures for England only); S Evans, *Further Analysis of IOP Community Data*, Report prepared for the Social Exclusion Unit (2004).

290. H Meltzer *et al*, *op. cit.*, 2002.

291. R Ford, A Beadsmore, P Norton *et al*, 'Developing Case Management for the Long-term Mentally Ill', *Psychiatric Bulletin of the Royal College of Psychiatry*, 17 (1994): 409-411, cited in J Repper and R Perkins, *op. cit.*, 2003.

292. V Pinfold, *Social Participation*. Report prepared for the Social Exclusion Unit by Rethink severe mental illness (2004).

293. Mind, *op. cit.*, 2004.

294. S Evans, *op. cit.*, 2004.

295 C Phillipson, G Allan and D Morgan, *Social Networks and Social Exclusion*, (Aldershot, Ashgate, 2004).

296. H Meltzer, *op. cit.*, 2003.

297. DJ Pevalin and D Rose, *Social capital for health: Investigating the links between social capital and health using the British Household Panel Survey*, (London, Health Development Agency, 2003).

298. T Becker, M Leese, P Clarkson, RE Taylor, D Turner, J Kleckham and G Thornicroft, 'Links between social networks and quality of life: An epidemiologically representative study of psychotic patients in South London', *Social Psychiatry and Psychiatric Epidemiology*, 33 (7) (1998): 299-304.

299. DJ Pevalin and D Rose, *op. cit.*, 2003.

300. Note that this refers to local initiatives and not the national TimeBank campaign referred to later in this chapter.

301. New Economics Foundation, *London Time Bank: Building London's Social Capital*, (London, New Economics Foundation, 2003).

302. V Pinfold, *op. cit.*, 2004.

303. E Seymour, L Gale and L Friedli, *Promoting Mental Health: A review of reviews*, (London, Mentality, 2003) unpublished.

304. HG Koenig, ME McCulloch and DB Larson, *Handbook of Religion and Health*, (Oxford, Oxford University Press, 2001).

305. Health Education Authority, *Promoting Mental Health: The role of faith communities – Jewish and Christian perspectives*, (London, Health Education Authority, 1999).

306. Mental Health Foundation, 'Spirituality and Mental Health', *Update*, Volume 4 Issue 6 (London, Mental Health Foundation, 2002).

307. Greater London Authority *Connecting People, Tackling Exclusion*, (London, GLA, 2003).

308. US National Organization on Disability, 2000 accessed at: http://www.nod.org/content.cfm?id=139.

309. D Piling, P Barrett and M Floyd, *Disabled People and the Internet: Experiences, Barriers and Opportunities*, (York, Joseph Rowntree Foundation, 2004).

310. Mind, *op. cit.*, 2004.

311. Quoted in J Read and S Baker, *op. cit.*, 1996.

312. A Falkov, *Crossing Bridges: Training Resources for Working with Mentally Ill Parents and their Children*, (London, Department of Health/Pavillion Publishing, 1998).

313. D Melzer *et al*, *op. cit.*, 2004.

314. Mental Health Foundation website, http://www.mentalhealth.org.uk/page.cfm?pagecode=PMNZPN.

315. M Oates, 'Postnatal mental illness: its importance and management', in M Gopfert, J Webster and MV Seeman (eds.), *Parental Psychiatric Disorder: Distressed parents and their families*, (Cambridge, Cambridge University Press, 1996).

316. A Falkov, *op. cit.*, 1998.

317. Quoted in A Weir and A Douglas, *Child Protection and Adult Mental Health: conflict of interest?*, (Oxford, Butterworth-Heinemann, 1992).

318. A Falkov, *op. cit.*, 1998.

319. J Aldridge and S Becker, *op. cit.*, 2003.

320. Social Care Institute for Excellence, *Alcohol, drug and mental health problems: working with families*, (London, Social Care Institute for Excellence, 2003).

321. Department of Health, *Getting Family Support Right: Inspection of the delivery of family support services,* (London, Department of Health, 1999).

322. B Isaac, E B Minty and R M Morrison, 'Children in care: the association with mental disorder in parents', *British Journal of Social Work,* 16 (1986):325-329.

323. J Read and S Baker, *op. cit.,* 1996.

324. J Aldridge and S Becker, *op. cit,* 2003.

325. Quoted in L Wardale and E Johnston, *Evaluation of the Family Room at Stoddart House,* (Liverpool, Save the Children, Barnardo's, Mersey Care Trust, Keeping the Family in Mind and Action with Young Carers, 2004).

326. J Morris, *op. cit.,* 2003.

327. N Singleton *et al, op. cit.,* 2002.

328. Quoted in P Corry, C Drury and V Pinfold, *Lost and Found: Voices from the Forgotten Generation,* (London, Rethink severe mental illness, 2004).

329. *Ibid.*

330. J Aldridge and S Becker, *op. cit.,* 2003.

331. A Falkov, *op. cit.,* 1998.

332. Institute for Volunteering Research, *Volunteering for Mental Health,* (London, National Centre for Volunteering, 2003).

333. This is not the same as the local Time Bank projects discussed earlier in the chapter.

334. National Centre for Volunteering, *You Cannot Be Serious: A Guide to Involving Volunteers with Mental Health Problems,* (London, National Centre for Volunteering, 2003).

335. Institute for Volunteering Research, *Volunteering and Mental Health: A Review of the Literature*, prepared for the Social Exclusion Unit (2003); P Bates, *A Real Asset: A Manual on Supported Volunteering,* (Manchester, National Development Team, 2002).

336. Disability Rights Commission Mental Health Action Group, *Twelve Key Priorities,* (2002) accessed at: http://www.drc-gb.org/whatwedo/MHAG1.asp.

337. Schedule 1, Juries Act 1974.

338. Disability Rights Task Force, *From Exclusion to Inclusion: Final report of the Disability Rights Taskforce,* (London, Disability Rights Task Force, 1999).

339. The Right Honourable Lord Justice Auld, *A Review of the Criminal Courts of England and Wales,* (London, Lord Chancellor's Department, 2001).

340. Department for Education and Skills, internal figures 2003.

341. School Governors' One-Stop Shop: Tel. (0870) 241 3883 or info@schoolgovernors-oss.co.uk; GovernorNet: www.governornet.co.uk.

342. School Governance (Constitution, Procedures and New Schools) (England) (Amendment) Regulations 2004. *'A person is disqualified from holding or continuing to hold office as a governor of a school at any time when he is detained under the Mental Health Act 1983.'*

343. F Aldridge and P Lavender, *Impact of Learning on Health,* (Leicester, National Institute for Adult Continuing Education, 1999).

344. C Hammond, *Learning to be Healthy,* Report to Department for Education and Skills by the Centre for Research in the Wider Benefits of Learning, Institute of Education, University of London, (Department for Education and Skills Research Brief No. RCB07, 2002).

345. H Meltzer, *op. cit.,* 2003. 28 per cent of people with common mental health problems have no qualifications, 6 per cent had qualifications equivalent to GCSE grades D-G, and 27 per cent had qualifications equivalent to GCSE grades A*-C. 15 per cent had A Levels, and 14 per cent had a degree. Among those with severe mental health problems, 38 per cent had no qualifications, 6 per cent had GCSEs grades D-G, and 32 per cent had GCSEs grades A*-C. 7 per cent had A Levels and 3 per cent had a degree.

346. P Seebohm *et al, op. cit.,* 2003.

347. Royal College of Psychiatrists, *The Mental Health of Students in Higher Education,* (London, Royal College of Psychiatrists, 2003).

348. Committee of Vice-Chancellors and Principals, *Guidelines on Student Mental Health Policies and Procedures for Higher Education,* (London, Universities UK, 2000).

349. Universities UK/SCOP Committee for the Promotion of Mental Well-being in Higher Education.

350. National Institute for Adult Continuing Education/National Institute for Mental Health in England Partnership Project, *Access to Adult Education for People with Mental Health Difficulties. Report of a National Postal Survey of Colleges of Further Education and Local Authority Adult Education Services*, (Leicester, National Institute for Adult Continuing Education/National Institute for Mental Health in England, 2003).

351. Individualised Student Record 22 (Further Education), *First Year UK Domiciled HE Students by Level of Study, Mode of Study, Gender and Disability 2001/2002*, Higher Education Statistics Agency.

352. B Andrews and JM Wilding, 'The Relation of Depression and Anxiety to Life Stress and Achievements in Students', paper presented to British Psychological Society, April 2004.

353. S Riddell, T Tinklin, and A Wilson, *Disabled Students and Multiple Policy Innovations in Higher Education. Final Report to the Economic and Social Research Council,* (2004).

354. H Meltzer, *op. cit.*, 2003.

355. A Killoran *et al*, *op. cit.*, 1994.

356. D Glenister, 'Exercise and Mental Health: A Review', *Journal of the Royal Society of Health*, February (1996): 7-13, quoted in A Faulkner and S Layzell, *Strategies for Living: A report of User-Led research into people's strategies for living with mental distress*, (London, The Mental Health Foundation, 2000).

357. F Matarasso, *Use or Ornament? The social impact of the Arts*, (Stroud, Comedia, 1997).

358. S Colgan, K Bridges and B Faragher, 'A tentative START to Community Care', *Psychiatric Bulletin,* 15 (1991): 596-8.

359. H Meltzer *et al*, *op. cit.*, 2002.

360. Shelter, *op. cit.*, 2003.

361. A Davis, *Mental Health and Personal Finances – A literature review*, prepared for the Social Exclusion Unit (2003); S Weich and G Lewis, 'Poverty, unemployment, and common mental disorders: population based cohort study', *British Medical Journal*, 317 (1998):115-119.

362. Office of the Deputy Prime Minister, *Homelessness Statistics: March 2004 and addressing the Health Needs of Homeless People,* Policy Briefing 7 (London, Office of the Deputy Prime Minister, 2004).

363. M Harrison and D Phillips, *Housing Black and Minority Ethnic Communities: Review of the evidence base*, (London, Office of the Deputy Prime Minister, 2003).

364. M Tarpey and L Watson, *Housing Need in Merton: People with severe mental illness living in households,* (London, London Borough of Merton,1997).

365. S Payne, *Poverty, Social Exclusion and Mental Health: Findings from the 1999 PSE survey. Working Paper no 15, Poverty and Social Exclusion Survey of Britain,* (Bristol, Townsend Centre for International Poverty Research, 2000).

366. Loonscape.com, *Consultation on mental health and social exclusion*, 2003.

367. S Edwards, *In Too Deep: CAB clients' experience of debt*, (London, Citizens Advice/Citizens Advice Scotland, 2003).

368. The IMS Money and Mental Health Survey (1999) cited in R Bundy, 'Mutual benefits', *Health Service Journal*, 111 (2001): 34.

369. H Meltzer *et al*, *op. cit.*, 2002.

370. S Payne, *op. cit.*, 2000.

371. A Davis, *op. cit.*, 2003.

372. *Ibid.*

373. R Knight, *Survey of Subscriber Institutions on Basic Bank Accounts*, (London, Banking Code Standards Board, 2003).

374. L Cullen, S Edwards, S Marks, L Phelps and J Sandbach, *Out of the picture: CAB evidence on mental health and social exclusion,* (London, Citizens Advice, 2004).

375. Office for National Statistics, *Disability Living Allowance Quarterly Statistics: August 2003,* (London, Office for National Statistics, 2003).

376. P Pleasance, A Buck, N Balmer, A O'Grady, H Genn and M Smith, *Causes of Action: Civil Law and Social Justice*, (London, The Stationery Office, 2004).

377. S Edwards, *op. cit.*, 2003.

378. J Read and S Baker, *op cit.*, 1996.

379. Association of British Insurers, *An Insurer's Guide to the Disability Discrimination Act (1995),* (London, Association of British Insurers, 2003).

380. Home Office, *Achieving Best Evidence in Criminal Proceedings: Guidance on vulnerable or intimidated witnesses including children*, (London, Home Office, 2002).

381. Home Office, *Statistics on Race and the Criminal Justice System 2002,* (London, Home Office, 2003).

382. Social Exclusion Unit, *op. cit.,* 2003.

383. Mind, *Concessionary travel and people with severe mental health problems: Evidence to the Disabled Persons Transport Advisory Committee*, (London, Mind, 2002).

384. For more details see Social Exclusion Unit, *Making the Connections: Final report on Transport and Social Exclusion*, (London, Office of the Deputy Prime Minister, 2003).

385. Focus on Mental Health, *An Uphill Struggle: Poverty and Mental Health*, (London, Mental Health Foundation, 2001).

386. Transport Act 2000.

387. Mind, *op. cit.,* 2002.

388. J Rankin and S Regan, *op. cit*, 2004.

389. The partner organisations are: LinkUp2 (supported employment project for employees of the NHS Trust and local authority), social services, Horizon House (Bromley's Clubhouse), Bromley FE and HE college, Orpington College, Bromley Mind, Status Employment (supported employment service), Bromley User Group, Community Links (volunteering service) and Bromley Jobcentre.

390. See Local Authority Circular 10, 2004.

391. See Local Authority Circular 7, 2004.

392. N Singleton, *A Comparison Between the Assessment of Mental Health Problems Obtained from the Long-standing Illness Question and Other Assessment Tools in the Survey of Psychiatric Morbidity Among Adults, 2000,* Paper prepared for the Social Exclusions Unit (2004).

393. T Thomas, T Ryan, K Newbigging, *SEU Consultation Exercise. Mental health, illness and social exclusion,* (London, Health and Social Care Advisory Service, 2003).